# THE FUTURE SUPPLY
# OF OIL AND GAS

# THE FUTURE SUPPLY OF oil

## AND gas

A STUDY OF THE AVAILABILITY
OF CRUDE OIL, NATURAL GAS,
AND NATURAL GAS LIQUIDS
IN THE UNITED STATES
IN THE PERIOD THROUGH 1975

BY **Bruce C. Netschert**

PUBLISHED FOR
RESOURCES FOR THE FUTURE, INC.
BY THE JOHNS HOPKINS PRESS, BALTIMORE

© 1958 by The Johns Hopkins Press, Baltimore 18, Md.

Distributed in Great Britain by Oxford University Press, London

Printed in the U.S.A. by American Book–Stratford Press

Library of Congress Catalog Card Number 58–7215

Second printing, 1958

## RESOURCES FOR THE FUTURE, INC., Washington, D. C.

Resources for the Future is a nonprofit corporation for research and education to advance development, conservation, and use of natural resources, primarily in the United States. It was established in 1952 with the cooperation of The Ford Foundation and its activities have been financed by grants from that Foundation. The main research areas of the resident staff are Water Resources, Energy and Mineral Resources, Land Use and Management, Regional Studies, and Resources and National Growth. One of the major aims of Resources for the Future is to make available the results of research by its staff members and consultants. Unless otherwise stated, interpretations and conclusions in RFF publications are those of the authors. The responsibility of the organization as a whole is for selection of significant questions for study and for competence and freedom of inquiry.

# Foreword

This study is part of a larger investigation of the energy position of the United States through 1975 which is being undertaken as part of the Energy and Minerals Program of Resources for the Future.

The author, Bruce C. Netschert, is a staff research associate in the energy and minerals area. Although he draws from a background of both geology and economics, his study is not intended as a technical contribution containing original geologic and engineering data. It is an economic study, based on the analysis and interpretation of technical opinion and the facts from which that opinion is derived. No prior knowledge of the oil and gas industry on the part of the reader is assumed.

The contributions of the study are of many kinds. At the most general level are the author's conclusions concerning oil and gas "availability" in 1975. This term is used in a special sense to include only the elements of physical availability and technologic feasibility bearing on future supply prospects. Demand and other important factors which will influence actual domestic production are excluded. Mr. Netschert concludes that in 1975, or thereabouts, domestic availability, at no appreciable increase in constant dollar costs, could be about 6 billion barrels of crude oil and 22.5 trillion cubic feet of natural gas per year. (Production in 1956 was 2.6 billion barrels of crude oil and 10.9 trillion cubic feet of natural gas.)

Such expectations range the author alongside the optimistic analysts of future oil and gas supply in the United States. As brought out in a survey of technical opinion in this study, many other students of the subject expect that peak production capabilities in the United States will be less than this, and that peak outputs will have been reached before 1975, with production of oil and gas already on the downswing by that time. Mr. Netschert's conclusions can not, however, be directly compared with the estimates of other authors, which are more in the nature of production forecasts. Because the above figures are estimates of availability, as that term has been defined here, they must not be construed as projections of actual output. The latter will depend upon demand and other considerations which are being analyzed in another part of our larger investigation of the United States energy position. The availability figures noted above can be translated into forecasts of production only in the larger perspective that includes demand and the intersubstitutability among all energy sources. This will be done in a forthcoming publication.

On a more specialized level the data and methods used in this study to analyze future availability are of considerable interest. These embody research materials and approaches which are significant by themselves, apart from the general conclusions they support.

Because a major determinant of future domestic production is the natural resource position of the United States in oil and gas, the author presents a systematic review of existing estimates of oil and gas reserves and resources, the techniques used in making the estimates, and the assumptions and definitions of terms upon which they are based. An attempt is made to achieve greater comparability among the estimates by adjusting them in accord with a set of uniform definitions which are relevant to the problem of studying long-run supply prospects. The author's accomplishments include the achievement of some degree of terminological standardization where there has heretofore been much vagueness and ambiguity; but further progress and agreement along these lines are sorely needed.

The chapters are characterized by an attempt to analyze the real variables—whether they be economic, technological, or geological—which will affect the future availability of oil and gas. There is thus a careful avoidance of the mechanical extrapolation of trends which too often has characterized studies of the future of oil and gas supply. A particular form of trend extrapolation which has found much favor in the literature of oil and gas projections is the so-called decline-curve analysis, which generalizes from the past production record of exhausted oil fields to obtain a curve which purports to describe the future national behavior of output. A cogent analysis of this technique is presented along with the author's reasons for rejecting it as a suitable tool for estimating future oil and gas production at the national level at this point in our oil and gas history. Among the author's major reasons for rejecting this technique is its static treatment of technology. In this report, technology is considered a dynamic factor of the first importance and its possible impact on future oil and gas availability is thoughtfully evaluated.

The inadequacy of some of the fundamental information on which the analysis of future supply must rest is regrettable. This is particularly true of the basic information on the country's natural wealth in oil and gas. Current data on this score are subject to the most severe limitations, since, by and large, they provide a measure only of proved reserves, i.e., discovered resources which can be recovered by currently utilized methods at current costs and prices (a quantity which, in oil, has for many years been the equivalent of about twelve times the annual production rate). The nation's resource base of oil and gas includes much more than these proved reserves, but there is no systematic body of knowledge about these "unproven" resources. No amount of careful sifting of existing data, nor of wisdom in evaluating the proper weight to be given to various factors likely to affect the situation in the future, can make up for this basic deficiency in our knowledge. Efforts to find feasible methods of filling the gaps in what is known about the nation's natural resource circumstances deserve the earnest attention of both industry and government.

The information contained in this book will be incorporated in a larger volume, which will be published upon completion of a group of RFF studies dealing with the over-all United States energy position through 1975. This publication procedure is being followed as a result of the response from individuals to whom a draft version of the present study was sent for expert review. In addition to many helpful criticisms and comments, Resources for the Future received suggestions that the study be made available in published form prior to completion of the larger project of which it is a part. We hope that the critical response to this publication will result in improving the quality and usefulness of the over-all study.

Sam H. Schurr, DIRECTOR
*Energy and Mineral Resources Program*

*January 3, 1958*

# Contents

## TABLES

# Acknowledgments

This work reflects in large measure the invaluable aid of my colleagues on the RFF staff. I am particularly indebted to Sam H. Schurr for his counsel and guidance. I wish also to express my appreciation to Orris C. Herfindahl and Joseph Lerner, whose thorough criticism was of great value in preparing the final draft.

The number of persons outside the RFF staff who assisted in the review of early drafts of this study is so large that it is not possible to list the specific benefit for which I am indebted to each individual. I acknowledge with thanks, however, the contributions of the following: Warren L. Baker, *World Oil* magazine; Austin Cadle, Standard Oil Co. of California; Ira H. Cram, Continental Oil Co.; Joel Dirlam, University of Connecticut; Richard J. Gonzalez, Humble Oil and Refining Co.; M. King Hubbert, Shell Development Co.; Alfred E. Kahn, Cornell University; S. G. Lasky, U. S. Department of the Interior; Paul W. McGann, U. S. Bureau of Mines; Eger V. Murphree, U. S. Department of Defense; Daniel Parson, American Gas Association; Wallace E. Pratt, Consultant; W. C. Schroeder, University of Maryland; P. R. Schultz, Blackwell Oil and Gas Co.; Lyon F. Terry, Chase Manhattan Bank; W. B. Tippy, Commonwealth Services, Inc.; Paul D. Torrey, Petroleum Engineer; Lewis G. Weeks, Standard Oil Co. of New Jersey; and Robert Wilson, Standard Oil Co. of Indiana.

In thanking these individuals, I wish to emphasize that

their presence in the list of acknowledgments does not imply necessary agreement with or approval of my opinions and conclusions. The responsibility is solely mine for all statements not quoted or attributed to other sources, and for all errors of fact or interpretation.

Bruce C. Netschert

# introduction

## PURPOSE AND METHODOLOGY

The future supply of energy in this country has been the subject of much attention in recent years, especially since the advent of the question of how nuclear power is likely to be integrated into the total supply of energy from various sources. A host of articles and several books have considered the subject from many viewpoints and, although a few rather narrow areas of agreement may be identified, the subject in general remains a field of active controversy. The present study, limited to crude oil, natural gas, and natural gas liquids availability, is offered with the hope that yet another look at the subject is justified in this instance by the use of concepts and an analytical approach that provide a new perspective and offer the possibility of widened areas of agreement.

It should be emphasized at the outset that the object of this study is *not* to arrive at forecasts or projections of future crude oil and natural gas *production* in this country. Such predictions have their usefulness in appropriate circumstances, but they are difficult to divorce from considerations of the demand that would call forth such levels of production. The course of future demand is a subject in itself. The analysis in this study is concerned with *availability*, which excludes the need for considering future demand. But demand is a deter-

1

minant of price, hence the latter must also be excluded. This can be done by seeking to answer the question: how much crude oil, natural gas, and natural gas liquids could be forthcoming in 1975 with no appreciable increase in constant dollar cost?

The factors that determine such future possible productive capacity are three: the natural stocks of these hydrocarbons, the technology of finding and producing them, and the course of production between now and 1975. The first two factors are discussed in the following pages; the third is most conveniently dealt with by an assumption, namely, that the growth in output between now and 1975 will be constant, by and large, whatever the possible productive capacity in the terminal year may be. This assumption requires that natural stocks be adequate to permit such growth—i.e., that production at no increase in costs will not be lower in 1975 than in some preceding year due to the depletion of natural stocks. The findings of this study on that score are, however, consistent with this requirement.

The terminal date of 1975 was chosen arbitrarily, for convenience. As a year marking a quarter of the twentieth century it is statistically neat. At the same time it has the advantage of being the reference year most used in discussions of the future of crude oil and natural gas in this country. This facilitates the examination and critical analysis of the various estimates of future crude oil and natural gas production in the United States.

This study is not concerned with the mechanical extrapolation of statistical trends. Many past studies have been preoccupied with such trends without paying much attention to the possible future behavior of the variables that determine the trends. The present work is in large part an examination of the variables.

The first section on each of the hydrocarbon raw materials is concerned with an estimation of the natural stock in the United States. Existing estimates are listed, described, and interpreted in the light of their demonstrated shortcomings. This is followed by a similar listing and description of existing estimates of future capacity and production in the period through 1975. The third section examines the indicated future course of technology and its relation to future productive capacity, and in the succeeding section the findings with respect to technology and the natural stock are applied to the existing estimates of future production and capacity to obtain an estimate of domestic availability in 1975. A final section considers briefly the possible role of alternative sources of supply: imports and synthetic equivalents.

## CONCEPTS AND DEFINITIONS CONCERNING

## RESERVES AND RESOURCES

In considering the source of the future supply of crude oil, natural gas, and natural gas liquids three concepts—"reserves," "resource base," and "resources"—are employed in this study and the terms are defined for present purposes. Conceptually, "reserves" are the stocks of a mineral raw material *in situ* as viewed by the operator producing it. In some instances, as in the coal industry, the term is not clearly defined and quantitative estimates are consequently rough. Elsewhere, as in the petroleum industry, the definition is rather carefully spelled out and quantitative figures have somewhat greater accuracy. Reserves are explicitly defined in terms of immediate or rather short-term economic feasibility of extraction. The cost limits are consistent with normal risk-taking and commercial production, and exclude material known to exist but which cannot be profitably extracted with *current* techniques. The broad usage of the term "reserves" in this study is consistent with industry definition.

Useful as this concept may be to those concerned with the actual production of mineral raw materials, it is unsatisfactory for the wider approach inherent in any view of the national economy as a whole. And it is decidedly inappropriate for any view that looks beyond the short term. A less restrictive concept and terminology is needed for the latter purpose.

The concept of a "resource base" is here proposed as a means of providing the needed perspective. The term is conceived to include the sum total of the crude oil, natural gas, and natural gas liquids present in the earth's crust within a geographic area. If reserves are denoted by A, the resource base, C, equals A plus B, where B comprehends all the stock not included in A, whether known or unknown and regardless of technologic feasibility of extraction and cost considerations. The resource base concept is thus absolute in that it includes *all* the occurrences within the geographic area specified. For the purposes of this study it comprehends the total quantities of the above named hydrocarbons present in the earth's crust within the area of the United States, including the adjacent continental shelf area.[1]

The reserve and resource base concepts establish the outer limits within which to consider the source of supply. The former is restricted to only what is known and economic; the

[1] The application of the resource base concept to other mineral raw materials, particularly to the metals, creates problems in defining the conceptual limits (although in the opinion of the author these can be successfully coped with). In the present instance, however, there are no such problems, and the conceptual limits are "clean." There is no question as to what should be included under the terms crude oil, natural gas, and natural gas liquids. There is no gradation in these hydrocarbon occurrences corresponding to the tenor of ore; a hydrocarbon occurrence is either one of these materials or it is not. The hydrocarbon content of such materials as bituminous shales or "tar sands," for example, is by universal custom excluded from the definition of petroleum. As for the environmental limits, these too are "clean" with respect to the hydrocarbons under consideration. Using the Mohorovičić discontinuity as the line of demarcation, the earth's crust underneath the continents is some 115,000 feet thick. But the theoretical limit to the possible depth of occurrence of the hydrocarbons is around 65,000 feet. (J. S. Cloninger, "How Deep Oil or Gas May Be Expected," *World Oil*, May, 1950, p. 60.) Although the maximum penetration to date is only one-third that depth, it is conceivable, even if not plausible, that technological progress could ultimately make penetration to such depths feasible. The resource base concept applied to crude oil, natural gas, and natural gas liquids therefore clearly comprehends the total occurrence of these hydrocarbons in the natural environment, and can be meaningfully related to technology.

latter passes over these two criteria and extends to the limits of the physical environment. Between these limits exists a wide middle ground where various technological and economic criteria may apply—where one may wish to consider "middle" quantities of the natural stocks coupled with technology and costs different from those currently prevailing.

The term "resources" is here employed to cover this middle ground. The "resources" of a mineral fuel may be defined according to the technical and economic criteria that are relevant and appropriate. The resources consist of that portion of the resource base (including reserves) which seems likely to become available given certain technological and economic conditions. The petroleum resources of the United States, for example, may be indicated as X billion barrels if one assumes that costs are triple those of the present and that there is full exploitation of the continental shelf, but only Y billion assuming a doubling of costs and a limitation of offshore operations to 200 feet of water. Or one may desire, as in the present study, to consider the natural stocks that could be exploited at about present costs with foreseeable technological advancement. Whether any particular definition of resources is useful depends on the context in which it is to be used, and the possibility and need for expressing it quantitatively.

Although the term "resource base" and the flexible definition of the term "resources" are here introduced for the first time,[2] the basic distinction between "reserves" and "resources" is not original. Present usage makes these terms interchangeable, but the distinction described was recently

[2] In his recent book, *Conservation in the Production of Petroleum* (New Haven: Yale University Press, 1957), E. W. Zimmermann also stresses the dynamic aspect of resources as the product of technology in defining resources as "environmental aspects for use by man" (p. 7). Zimmermann relates resources solely to need, however, rather than to their availability as determined by technology. His concept thus has elements of both "resources" and the "resource base" as here defined. Moreover, he does not attempt to relate his resource concept to the conventional reserve concept, nor does he consider the possibility or usefulness of quantifying petroleum resources in estimates.

proposed as part of a trenchant terminological analysis in a report by an international committee of geologists.[3]

The author acknowledges his debt to this committee report, and suggests that his own terminological innovations add logical completeness to the concepts and definitions set forth in the report. The application of the new concepts and definitions to the specific hydrocarbon categories of crude oil, natural gas, and natural gas liquids constitutes the initial subject in the discussion of each of the three categories. It should be noted that the above specific definitions are applied herein to a body of information which is not set forth with equivalent precision in meaning. The results are therefore less than perfect—ambiguities in the literature cannot be wholly cleared up, and the figures employed are not always satisfactory measures in that they do not correspond completely to the definitions. Nevertheless, the introduction of terminological precision is believed to be a desirable end in itself, and it is hoped that its use in the present study has contributed to a better understanding of the subject.

[3] F. Blondel and S. G. Lasky, "Mineral Reserves and Mineral Resources," *Economic Geology*, LI, No. 7 (November, 1956), 686-97.

# I

# crude oil

## ESTIMATES OF RESERVES

This section surveys the opinion of technical authorities within the industry on the present United States reserve-resource position in petroleum. At the start it is necessary to relate the industry terminology in which existing estimates are presented to the terminology outlined in the Introduction.

The term "reserves" as used in the petroleum industry is normally a contraction of the term "proved recoverable reserves." The American Petroleum Institute provides an authoritative and explicit definition as follows:

> Proved reserves are both drilled and undrilled. The proved drilled reserves, in any pool, include oil estimated to be recoverable by the production systems now in operation, whether with or without fluid injection, and from the area actually drilled up on the spacing pattern in effect in that pool. The proved undrilled reserves, in any pool, include reserves under undrilled spacing units which are so close, and so related, to the drilled units that there is every reasonable probability that they will produce when drilled.[1]

Although additions to proved reserves can accrue through improved recovery techniques, through more favorable eco-

[1] Committee on Petroleum Reserves, *1957 Report* to the American Petroleum Institute, March 6, 1957.

nomic conditions, or through better knowledge of the reservoirs in which the oil occurs, the magnitude of proved reserves at any point in time is in the last analysis a function of the drilling of wells. And, since the industry is interested in production, not in the proving of reserves for their own sake (which would involve the tying up of large capital sums), the ratio of proved reserves to production tends to be small. Proved reserves as of the end of 1956 were 30.4 billion barrels, 11.9 times production in that year. In the period since 1946 the proved reserves-production ratio has averaged 12.4, ranging from a high of 13.6 to a low of 11.6

In the numerous discussions of the probable course of future oil discoveries in this country the tendency has been, with few exceptions, to hold technology as well as costs constant, either explicitly or implicitly. These discussions have commonly employed the term "ultimate reserves," meaning all oil so far produced, plus current proved reserves, plus "reserves" (defined in terms of current technology and costs) that will be discovered in the future.

In order to review only current opinion in the present study the literature, save for a few exceptions, has been surveyed only for 1950 and subsequent years. For convenience, the estimates are first examined and compared on an ultimate-reserve basis. But it is evident that this basis, by limiting technology to its current status, ignores the element of technological progress in the determination of future productive capacity. When used as a basis for estimating future production and future resource positions there is a strong downward bias.

There is, of course, a legitimate and proper use for a reserve concept even as restrictive as proved reserves. But it is certainly illogical, in estimating the course of future production, to assume that technology remains frozen. Estimates on this basis may be admissible if presented as minimal figures because of the definitional restriction on technology (although most estimates are unaccompanied by this caveat); yet the fact remains that they represent only a partial, incomplete look at the future.

It is necessary, therefore, in line with the concepts used herein, to convert the ultimate-reserve estimates into resource base figures. It is believed that this conversion is accomplished below without violating the essential meaning and intent of the authors of the ultimate-reserve estimates. The advantage gained is the very large one of subsequently being able to introduce into the all-inclusive resource-base concept the limitations of technology that appear as plausible and probable future developments. The procedure followed is somewhat circuitous, but it is hoped that as the exposition proceeds the benefits of its use will be apparent. The final result is that the conclusions arrived at in this study, although based on new and different concepts, also reflect the opinion of recognized authorities who have employed the conventional concept.

In order to compare and examine the various estimates, certain distinctions must be recognized. One of these is the conventional one between "primary" and "secondary" production. Broadly speaking, primary production is that obtained through the development, by drilling, of an oil reservoir. Such production may be accompanied by recycling the associated natural gas back into the reservoir to maintain pressure. And as a further means of increasing the total cumulative recovery of the oil in the reservoir, such production may be aided by "fluid injection," defined by the American Petroleum Institute as "a method of recovery of oil, gas and/or related hydrocarbons in which part of the energy effective in moving these hydrocarbons through a reservoir is applied from extraneous sources by injection of liquids or gases into the reservoir." [2]

Primary production with fluid injection is obtained when the technique is applied "early in the producing life of a reservoir when there has been little or no loss of natural reservoir energy." In contradistinction, "secondary recovery is an application of fluid injection when a reservoir is approaching or has reached economic production limits." [3]

[2] P. D. Torrey, "Significance of Fluid Injection in United States Oil Fields," *The Oil Forum*, x, No. 12 (Mid-November, 1956), 425.
[3] *Idem.*

A second distinction can be made between "continental," or "onshore," oil and "offshore" oil. The offshore oil occurs under submerged lands of the continental shelf and is obtainable only through specialized techniques of directional drilling and drilling in open water.

In order to aid the analysis of the estimates of future reserves, these production categories are translated into the following reserve categories:

(a) "primary reserves"—obtainable through primary onshore production
(b) "secondary reserves"—obtainable through secondary onshore production
(c) "offshore reserves"—as defined above (and including oil obtainable through secondary production offshore)

The published estimates fail to recognize or specify these distinctions in many instances and are thus frequently ambiguous or even wholly lacking definition. Whether or not an estimate so states, for example, it is likely to include an indeterminate proportion of secondary reserves if it was derived from data on proved reserves, since the latter include a varying but indeterminate proportion of secondary reserves. Nevertheless, the several estimates have been brought together in Table 1 and listed under what seems to be the appropriate reserve category. Where possible the estimate is shown for comparison purposes as an "ultimate reserves" figure, which is further related to a quantity "yet to be produced" (as of January 1, 1957), and the ratio of this unproduced total to 1956 output.

Because of ambiguity and lack of definition, the placement of many of the estimates in the respective reserve category in Table 1 as well as the conversion to an ultimate-reserves figure may involve considerable error or distortion of the original intent or meaning behind the estimate. Nevertheless it is believed that the presentation is in general sufficiently faithful to provide a useful basis for analyzing published opinion.[4]

[4] This study has had the benefit of comments from most of the authors whose estimates are listed in Table 1.

TABLE 1

## Estimates of Future Crude Oil Reserves
## of the United States

(In billion barrels)

| Source and date (1) | Primary (2) | Secondary (resources) (3) | Off-shore (4) | Ultimate (5) | Yet to be produced (1/1/57) (6) | Col. 6 as multiple of 1956 production (7) |
|---|---|---|---|---|---|---|
| Weeks, 1948 (a) | 110 (165)† | — | — | — | — | — |
| Pratt, 1950 (b) | 109 | — | 33* | 142* | 87 | 33 |
| U.S.G.S., 1951 (c) | — | — | >15 | — | — | — |
| Thompson, 1951 (d) | — | 75 | — | — | — | — |
| Egloff, 1951 (e) | 500-1,000 | — | 500-1,000 | 1,000-2,000 | 945-1,945 | 363-748 |
| Murphree, 1953 (f) | — | 111 | — | — | — | — |
| Petersen, 1952 (g) | — | 69 | — | — | — | — |
| Schultz, 1952 (h) | 170 | ——30—— | | >200 | 145 | 56 |
| Carmical, 1955 (i) | — | — | >15 | — | — | — |
| Ayres, 1955 (j) | — | — | — | 140 | 86 | 33 |
| Interior Dept., 1956 (k) | — | — | — | 300 | 246 | 95 |
| Pogue & Hill, 1956 (l) | — | — | — | 165 | 111 | 43 |
| Murrell, 1956 (m) | — | — | — | 200 | 145 | 56 |
| Hubbert, 1956 (n) | 130 | — | 20 | 150 | 95 | 37 |
| Torrey, 1956 (o) | — | 33 (99)‡ | — | — | — | — |
| Hill et al., 1957 (p) | — | — | 20 | >250 | 195 | 75 |

* Imputed.
† See text, p. 13.
‡ See text, p. 16.

SOURCES:

(a) L. G. Weeks, "Highlights on 1947 Developments in Foreign Petroleum Fields," *Bulletin,* American Association of Petroleum Geologists, XXXII, No. 6, p. 1094.

(b) W. E. Pratt, "The Earth's Petroleum Resources," *Our Oil Resources,* ed. L. M. Fanning (2nd ed.; New York: McGraw-Hill Book Co., 1950), p. 151.

(c) United States Geological Survey, *Fuel Reserves of the United States,* Senate Committee on Interior and Insular Affairs, 82nd Congress, 1st Session (Washington, D. C.: U. S. Government Printing Office, 1951).

As a first step in the analysis, the estimates under the respective reserve categories are described in chronological order. (Unless otherwise specified in a footnote, a reference to the original estimate may be assumed to be that listed in Table 1.)

## Primary Reserves

The estimate by Weeks, although made prior to 1950, is included because it is a reference mark for subsequent estimates. Weeks' figure is based on a systematic analysis of the various sedimentary basins and oil provinces of the world.

---

SOURCES, TABLE 1, (CONTD.):

(d) E. O. Thompson, "Freedom's Oil," *Proceedings,* American Petroleum Institute, XXXII, No. 1 (1952), 32.

(e) G. Egloff, "Oil and Gas as Industrial Raw Materials," *Resources for Freedom,* Report of the President's Materials Policy Commission (Washington, D. C.: U. S. Government Printing Office, 1952), IV, 193.

(f) E. V. Murphree, "Where Will Tomorrow's Oil Come From?" *Oil and Gas Journal,* November 3, 1952, pp. 123 f.

(g) T. S. Petersen, "Oil in the Next Quarter-Century," *Proceedings,* American Petroleum Institute, XXXII, No. 1 (1952), 32.

(h) P. R. Schultz, "What Is the Future of Petroleum Discovery?" *Oil and Gas Journal,* July 28, 1952, p. 259.

(i) J. H. Carmical, *New York Times,* August 7, 1955.

(j) E. Ayres, "Energy Resources for the Future," *Oil and Gas Compact Bulletin,* XIV, No. 1 (June, 1955), 20.

(k) Joint Committee on Atomic Energy, *Peaceful Uses of Atomic Energy,* Report of the Panel on the Impact of Peaceful Uses of Atomic Energy (Washington, D. C.: U. S. Government Printing Office, January, 1956), II, 82.

(l) J. E. Pogue and K. E. Hill, *Future Growth and Financial Requirements of the World Petroleum Industry* (New York: Chase Manhattan Bank, 1956). Presented at annual meeting of the American Institute of Mining, Metallurgical and Petroleum Engineers, Petroleum Branch, February 21, 1956.

(m) J. H. Murrell, as reported in *Petroleum Week,* March 16, 1956, pp. 9 f.

(n) M. K. Hubbert, "Nuclear Energy and the Fossil Fuels," *Drilling and Production Practice—1956* (New York: American Petroleum Institute, 1957), pp. 14 f.

(o) P. D. Torrey, "Evaluation of U. S. Oil Resources as of January 1, 1956," *Producers Monthly,* June, 1956, pp. 26, 28.

(p) K. E. Hill, H. D. Hammar, and J. G. Winger, "Future Growth of the World Petroleum Industry," paper presented at the meeting of the American Petroleum Institute Division of Production, Rocky Mountain District, Casper, Wyoming, April 25, 1957.

"Preliminary and basic studies include the origin and development of basins, and their classification based on origin, history, physical form or architecture and composition. They involve a study of sedimentation and deposition environment, the effects of the changes that occur progressively with different stages of the deposition cycle." [5] These studies were used to obtain an estimate of the "potential ultimate recoverable oil" from individual sedimentary areas and basins, using as guides or bases for comparison measurements of productivity from current or previously producing units of the earth's crust. These measurements were in the form of barrels of oil per square mile, per cubic mile, per unit of exploratory effort and the like.

Weeks' estimate was originally presented as the amount of undiscovered recoverable reserves as of 1948, which he concluded were about equal to past discoveries. Secondary reserves were not meant to be included,[6] and offshore reserves were explicitly excluded. Weeks considers that, although he has gone beyond the proved reserve concept in his figure, the conclusion is a very conservative one, and the final figure for primary production from the land area of the United States is more likely to be 50 per cent larger, or 165 billion barrels, than 10 per cent less.

Pratt's estimate, like that of Weeks, is based on geological inference. But whereas Weeks uses a detailed analysis of individual petroliferous areas, Pratt relies on a general relationship between production and areal extent of production. Excluding the offshore province, he estimates reserves of 100 billion barrels based on the extent and productivity of proved producing areas. Assuming on the basis of past experience that some 1.5 per cent of the "distinctly favorable" parts of the total United States area (amounting to about 577 million acres) were eventually productive, such productive area would total

[5] L. G. Weeks, discussion in *Proceedings,* United Nations Scientific Conference on Conservation and Utilization of Resources (New York: United Nations, 1950), I, 108.
[6] Personal communication.

8.6 million acres. Cumulative discoveries through 1948 totaled 57.2 billion barrels from a producing area of 4.5 million acres, hence reserves (excluding the continental shelf) would be about 109 billion barrels (rounded in Pratt's presentation to an even 100 billion).[7]

Egloff cites Weeks' estimate of 100 billion barrels (as originally presented, in round numbers) and points out that this quantity of oil would occupy somewhat less than 4 cubic miles. If the estimate were correct, it would mean that 4 cubic miles of oil would be produced from 1.5 million cubic miles of sediments. In Egloff's view this is disproportionately small; the ultimate reserves of the land area of the United States are more likely to range between 500 and 1,000 billion barrels, or 20 to 40 cubic miles of oil from 1.5 million cubic miles of sediments.

Schultz's estimate of 170 billion barrels is based on a projection of the "trend of cumulative discoveries." Although he does not specify what this means it is probable that he applied a logistic growth curve to the cumulative discovery statistics. Such a curve yields an upper asymptote which represents the ultimate total. Schultz implies that with existing data the asymptote is still ambiguous by noting that his figure is a "minimum ultimate potential" and that it will probably continue to grow.

Hubbert's estimate is a modification of Weeks' original figure based on the good production record of the past two decades made possible through improved recovery practices.

---

[7] A later estimate by Pratt appears in the report of the Panel on the Impact of the Peaceful Uses of Atomic Energy (Joint Committee on Atomic Energy, *Peaceful Uses of Atomic Energy* [Washington, D. C.: U. S. Government Printing Office, January, 1956], II, 94). The estimate of 170 billion barrels as the ultimate reserves of the United States is in terms of "liquid hydrocarbons," which includes Natural Gas Liquids (see Section III of this study). Although it is possible to assume a certain proportion of the latter in the total figure on the basis of statistical relationships, Pratt gives no indication as to what proportion is subsumed in his estimate. In the absence of such knowledge it is considered here that the assumption of any given proportion would be an unwarranted interpretation of Pratt's figure. The estimate is therefore omitted from discussion in this study.

*Secondary "Reserves"*

Consideration of the basis of future secondary production again calls attention to the reserve-resource distinction discussed in the opening paragraphs of this study. The authors who have made specific estimates of future total secondary recovery allow for improved recovery methods or more favorable economic conditions—criteria used herein as part of the definition of "resources." For this reason the heading of this section has been put in quotation marks and the word "resources" is in parentheses above column 3 of Table 1.

Thompson's estimate of secondary resources is not supported by any argument. He merely remarks that possible secondary recovery might be as high as 75 billion barrels.

Murphree's estimate is accompanied by more detail. He notes that in 1950 the estimated oil content of known fields was 175 billion barrels. Of this, 64 billion barrels could be expected through primary recovery and 4 billion more through conventional secondary methods such as water flooding. The remaining 107 billion barrels await improved secondary recovery methods, and "there is indication that secondary methods will be developed in the future that will be able to recover the bulk of this remaining oil." [8] This yields a secondary-resource estimate composed of 4 billion barrels of reserves and 107 billion that will ultimately become reserves because of technological progress. Technically, however, it is not a complete secondary-resource estimate because it does not include the undiscovered oil that will be producible only through secondary operations. It could perhaps be termed "known secondary resources."

Petersen's estimate is apparently a passing reference to the Murphree figure. Petersen forecasts that secondary recovery will yield 65 billion barrels of the total known 107 billion barrels unrecoverable in 1950. The 4 billion of Murphree's

[8] E. V. Murphree, "Where Will Tomorrow's Oil Come From?" *Oil and Gas Journal*, November 3, 1952, pp. 119-24.

secondary reserves has been added to Petersen's 65 billion barrels in Table 1. Again, this estimate provides only a figure for known secondary resources.

The Torrey estimate is the latest of several he has presented in recent years as part of comprehensive, continuing statistical work by the Interstate Oil Compact Commission Committee on Secondary Recovery and Pressure Maintenance. The work involves a field-by-field study of the oil fields of the United States. The committee estimates the original oil content of known reservoirs to have been 288.5 billion barrels.[9] After primary production under present economic and technological conditions some 194 billion barrels of this total would remain unrecovered. Of this amount, according to the committee, about 12 billion barrels can be recovered with known secondary methods under economic conditions as of January 1, 1956 (i.e., secondary reserves are 12 billion barrels). Under "optimum economic conditions" and known methods, however, a total of 33 billion barrels could be recovered.[10] This is in a sense a resource estimate although based on current technology, and is accordingly listed in Table 1. Torrey has stated more recently that "under optimum conditions this figure might be trebled," [11] and a figure of 99 billion barrels has therefore been placed in parentheses in Table 1.

*Offshore "Reserves"*

Again the term "reserves" must be put in quotation marks in the heading, since some of the estimates include offshore oil beyond the water depth limits of current technology.

The figure of 33 billion barrels attributed to Pratt in Table 1 is a double inference; it is not an actual estimate by him. Pratt's only figure for the continental shelf area is one trillion

[9] P. D. Torrey, "Evaluation of U. S. Oil Resources as of January 1, 1956," *Producers Monthly*, June, 1956, pp. 26, 28.

[10] *Idem;* also P. D. Torrey, "Significance of Fluid Injection in United States Oil Fields," *The Oil Forum*, x, No. 12 (Mid-November, 1956), 428.

[11] Personal communication.

barrels for the earth as a whole, based on the recoverable oil content per unit volume of sediments in the United States applied to the volume of the continental shelves of the world. Taking the United States and Alaskan portion of the total shelf area of the world as 10 per cent, the Geological Survey suggests that it is possible to infer from Pratt's estimate a figure of 100 billion barrels.[12] The figure for the United States alone was obtained for this study by taking the same ratio between Alaska and the United States continental shelf areas as was used by the Geological Survey in their inference from the Weeks figure.

The Survey does not offer its own estimate for the total continental shelf area of the United States but considers, on the basis of discoveries to date in coastal Texas and Louisiana, that their offshore resources approximate 13 billion barrels, and by similar reasoning the California offshore resources are some 2 billion barrels. "It should be emphasized, however, that these two areas probably have greater oil and gas possibilities than any other parts of the Continental Shelf adjacent to the United States." [13]

Egloff concludes that as much oil will probably be found under the continental shelves as will be produced under the land areas. He cites a figure of 14 million square miles, however, as the area of the continental shelves bordering the United States as the basis for this conclusion. This makes his estimate invalid, since the figure pertains to the total continental shelf area of the world, not that of the United States alone.

Carmical's estimate is derived from industry geologists' opinion plus his own judgment.[14] According to him, the total off-

[12] United States Geological Survey, *Fuel Reserves of the United States,* Senate Committee on Interior and Insular Affairs, 82nd Congress, 1st Session (Washington, D. C.: U. S. Government Printing Office, 1951), p. 32.
The Survey also suggests the inference of a figure of 12 billion barrels for the United States continental shelf area from an estimate by Weeks for the total of the world's continental shelf area. Weeks, however, denies the implication and strongly criticizes the procedure of assuming the same area-occurrence ratio for different areas of the world. (Personal communication.)
[13] *Idem.*
[14] Personal communication.

shore reserves out to a depth of 250 feet of water are estimated to be over 15 billion barrels, based on 300 discoveries to date and known production and proved reserve data for adjacent shore areas.

Hubbert cites the Geological Survey offshore estimate together with an estimate for California, by Jenkins of the California Division of Natural Resources, which is larger by 2 billion barrels than the Survey figure. This total of 17 billion barrels is rounded to 20 billion by Hubbert.

The estimate of 20 billion barrels by Hill *et al.* is merely mentioned by them as included in their ultimate reserve estimate.

### Ultimate Reserves

The Pratt figure for ultimate reserves in Table 1 is derived, as noted above, through the addition to his "basic" estimate of a figure for offshore resources inferred from his published statements. It is therefore an imputed figure, as noted in Table 1, not an estimate specifically made by Pratt.

The Egloff estimate, presented as a range, is merely the equivalent of his statement that offshore reserves equal onshore reserves.

Schultz bases his estimate on a projection of the trend of cumulative discoveries plus an estimate for secondary recovery and offshore potential. He considers this a minimum that will probably grow in the future.

Ayres' estimate is stated as follows: "Using Weeks' estimates including both on- and off-shore oil (*sic*), adjusted to January 1, 1955, and the A.P.I. evaluation of proved reserves, it seems that we may have about 90 billion barrels of oil yet to be produced . . ." [15] Together with cumulative past production, this is the equivalent of a total of 140 billion barrels through time. Ayres had previously taken note of Schultz's 200-billion barrel estimate, contending that such higher estimates of the ulti-

[15] E. Ayres, "Energy Resources for the Future," *Oil and Gas Compact Bulletin,* XIV, No. 1 (June, 1955), 20.

mate reserve are not based on firm physical data but "on a passionate desire to postpone the time when production will be inadequate." [16]

The Interior Department estimate prepared for the Panel on the Impact of Peaceful Uses of Atomic Energy is derived from the Schultz estimate, modified by the considerations that "trends in production and discovery are still headed upward, and that significant improvements in recoverability are now being accomplished or promised for the future . . ." [17] In the terminology of this paper this is clearly a resource estimate because of the allowance for improved technology.

The estimate by Pogue and Hill is included in Table 1 only because it is the basis of their projection of future production. It is actually not an estimate but merely the assumption that future discoveries will equal past discoveries. No justification is offered for the choice of this particular assumption.

Murrell's estimate of 200 billion barrels represents his judgment compared to other estimates in the 160-165 billion barrel range. He considers these too small in the light of the production record, which has thus far surpassed all earlier estimates of reserves.

The supporting data and arguments for Hubbert's estimate of 150 billion barrels as the ultimate reserve have been referred to above, under the individual reserve components.

In making their estimate of 250 billion barrels Hill *et al.* refer to the previous Pogue and Hill estimate as a minimum one, acknowledge that other recent estimates have ranged between 200 and 300 billion barrels, and "accept as plausible" a figure of 250 billion barrels.

## Reserve Estimates and the Resource Base

As shown in Table 2, the ultimate-reserve estimates may be divided into three groups: those below 200 billion barrels,

[16] E. Ayres, "U. S. Oil Outlook: How Coal Fits In," *Coal Age,* LVIII, No. 8 (August, 1953), 72.
[17] Joint Committee on Atomic Energy, *op. cit.*, II, 81 f.

TABLE 2

*Estimates of Ultimate Reserves of Crude Oil in*
*the United States Arranged in Order of Size*

(In billion barrels)

| Source | Estimate |
| --- | --- |
| Egloff | 1000–2000 |
| Interior Department | 300 |
| Hill *et al.* | >250 |
| Schultz | >200 |
| Murrell | 200 |
| Pogue & Hill | 165 |
| Hubbert | 150 |
| Pratt | 142 |
| Ayres | 140 |

those in the 200-300 billion range, and the single estimate in the range of trillions of barrels. (The individual estimates in columns 3 and 4 of Table 1 will not be discussed here, for reasons that will shortly become apparent.) Among the estimators only Pratt (in his "basic" figure) has attempted a systematic derivation of an ultimate-reserve figure from the circumstances of natural occurrence. The others either derive such a figure from discovery statistics, proclaim a figure as their flat judgment, or use their judgment to modify Weeks' or Pratt's original conclusions.

It is unfortunate that Weeks did not see fit to carry his estimate of primary reserves through to an ultimate-reserve estimate. It is the only primary estimate not represented in the ultimate-reserve column of Table 1. Not only is it the pioneer estimate, but of all those in Table 1 it presents the most comprehensive and systematic analysis. Weeks' estimate is derived from the sum of geologic knowledge concerning the quantitative and areal occurrence of petroleum, plus production experience to date. Its basis is a detailed and exhaustive examination of the volumetric relationships between oil occurrence and sediments. Nevertheless, the extrapolation of these data is inevitably so open-ended that the predominant element in the estimate is, in the last analysis, the estimator's individual judgment.

All of the estimates involving undiscovered oil are thus individual interpretations which are subject to large error. This is not meant to be an invidious judgment; it is a statement with which the authors listed would be the first to agree.

It remains now to consider the ultimate-reserve estimates in terms of the resource-base concept as set forth earlier in this study. For convenience and simplicity the estimates were discussed in their own terms but, as noted above, these terms carry with them the concept of proved reserves and its limiting criterion of current technology. Even when Weeks, for example, speaks of the "potential ultimate recoverable oil" he is basing his estimate on area-productivity relationships *measured in terms of proved reserves*, hence under current technology. On the other hand, with the resource-base concept one can view the "oil environment," so to speak, within which future technology will operate.

The translation from ultimate reserves to the resource base can be accomplished directly and simply by means of the "recovery factor," which is the percentage of the total oil content of the reservoir which can be recovered over the producing life of that reservoir. The relation is as follows:

(a) Ultimate-reserve estimates are based on the proved-reserve concept.

(b) Proved reserves are defined in terms of current recovery (i.e., only that oil is included which is recoverable with current technology).

(c) Therefore, to convert an ultimate-reserve estimate (A) into an inferred resource-base equivalent (C) (see p. 4), the formula is

$$C = \frac{A}{\text{recovery factor}}$$

A figure frequently used in the literature as the average recovery factor (including primary and secondary) in the United States today is 40 per cent. The author has not been able to find a substantiation of it, however, and dismisses it in favor of the estimate by the Interstate Oil Compact Commission Committee on Secondary Recovery and Pressure Maintenance. According to the Committee, under the conditions (technological and economic) prevailing at the end of 1956 there would be an ultimate recovery of 32.7 per cent of the original oil in place from known reservoirs.[18] This figure is an average of data from a field-by-field study of the oil fields of the United States and is derived from information from the files and records of the various state regulatory authorities not available to any other investigators. But since the current recovery factor cannot really be known with a precision of one-tenth of one per cent, it may be said that to the best of current knowledge recovery averages about one-third of the total oil present in a reservoir.

Under the procedure outlined above, the ultimate-reserve estimates are multiplied by a factor of three (the reciprocal of the recovery factor) to obtain an inferred resource-base equivalent. The results when applied to the estimates in Table 2 are listed in Table 3. Because of its magnitude and ambiguous basis, the Egloff estimate does not seem suitable for conversion. The Interior Department estimate contains an unspecified allowance for improvement in recovery, hence cannot be converted. The conversion of the remaining estimates is not considered to do violence to the originals since all of them are based, either explicitly or implicitly, on current recoverability.

A few words of caution and qualification are, however, in order. First, multiplication by three on the basis of a recovery factor of approximately one-third does *not* carry any implications concerning the future recovery level. The conversion in Table 3 merely shows the equivalent resource base inferable from the respective ultimate-reserve estimates. Second, the ad-

[18] P. D. Torrey, "Evaluation of U. S. Oil Resources as of January 1, 1956," *Producers Monthly*, June, 1956, pp. 26, 28. Also personal communication.

jective "equivalent" is used advisedly. The result is not, in fact, the total resource base. Only recovery technology is taken into account by conversion, whereas the total resource base could be obtained from the estimates only by taking account of the fact that current discovery and drilling technology is not able

TABLE 3

*Estimates of "Ultimate Reserves" Converted to Inferred "Resource Base" Equivalent*

(In billion barrels)

| Source and date (1) | "Ultimate reserve" estimate (2) | Inferred equivalent "resource base" (3) | Yet to be discovered (1/1/56) (4) | Possibly available for future recovery (5) |
|---|---|---|---|---|
| Hill *et al.* | 250 | 750 | 462 | 697 |
| Schultz, 1952 | >200 | >600 | >312 | >547 |
| Murrell, 1956 | 200 | 600 | 312 | 547 |
| Pogue & Hill, 1956 | 165 | 495 | 207 | 442 |
| Hubbert, 1956 | 150 | 450 | 162 | 397 |
| Pratt, 1950 | 142 | 426 | 138 | 373 |
| Ayres, 1955 | 140 | 420 | 132 | 367 |

SOURCES: See Table 1.

to probe the limits of the petroleum environment. The results of the conversion thus logically apply only to the crude oil that exists down to the current depth limit of drilling, since the ultimate-reserve estimates do not suggest the eventual probing of the total environment in which petroleum may possibly occur. Nevertheless, with due allowance for the shortcomings of the conversion procedure, its application to the ultimate-reserve estimates gives inferred resource-base equivalents that are sufficiently useful for present purposes by indicating the general order of magnitude of the resource base that can be inferred.

In column 4 of Table 3 the resource-base figures are reduced by the original oil content of known reservoirs (i.e., all oil discovered in the United States to date), estimated to be 288 billion barrels.[19] This yields the oil yet to be discovered according to the various estimates. Column 5 of Table 3 is obtained by subtracting from the figures in column 3 the total production through 1955, or 53 billion barrels. (1956 production is not included because the estimate of original oil content is as of January 1, 1956.) The figures in column 5, adapted to the conceptual basis of this study, thus present the total quantity of oil from which future production will come as inferred from expert opinion on ultimate reserves.

The conclusion from Table 3 is that the resource base for future oil production in this country is on the general order of magnitude of 500 billion barrels. It is worth repeating what this means so that the reader will avoid the error of interpreting it in the light of conventional concepts.

*The total crude oil awaiting (potentially available for) future recovery in the United States can be inferred from expert opinion to be on the order of 500 billion barrels. This includes present proved reserves, the currently unrecoverable content of known reservoirs, and the total content of undiscovered reservoirs, without regard to present or future technologic feasibility of discovery and recovery.*[20]

---

[19] *Idem.*

[20] It must be noted that this approach and the resulting conclusion are anticipated in the following succinct statement: "Scientific estimates of ultimate production appear to be based on recovering only about 40 per cent of the oil in place, reflecting past experience and current practices. Estimates that ultimate production will be 200-300 billion barrels of oil really indicate discovery of reservoirs with 500-700 billion barrels of oil in place." (R. J. Gonzalez, "U. S. Not Running Out of Oil," *World Oil*, 144, No. 4 [March, 1957], 66.) Nevertheless, the full implications of this conclusion, especially in terms of the results of increased recovery over the medium term, have not, in this writer's opinion, received the recognition they deserve.

# ESTIMATES OF FUTURE CAPACITY

# AND PRODUCTION

Just as authoritative opinion on future reserves was examined as an aid in estimating the resource base, so it is useful to examine opinion on future production and productive capacity in estimating the future availability of oil from domestic sources. The various published estimates of future annual production and/or capacity during the period through 1975 are brought together for this purpose in Table 4.

There is less ambiguity here than in the reserve estimates, although there is one aspect in which the use of the estimates may be inconsistent with the authors' original intentions. Most of the estimates are forecasts or projections of actual United States crude oil production for a given year or years in the future. As production estimates they carry certain assumptions about the demand which would call forth such production and about an import level that would supplement that production in meeting the demand; they are thus not necessarily estimates of *availability* as considered in this study. At the same time there is an availability implication in the estimates—if a forecaster believes production in a certain year will be X billion barrels, it seems proper to conclude that in his opinion the potential capacity for that year should be *at least* that same X billion barrels. Thus the various estimates of production can be used to give an indication of expert opinion as to the general level of crude oil availability from domestic production. The perspective of availability *ex demand* used in this study can then be applied.

TABLE 4

## *Estimates of Future Crude Oil Capacity and/or Production in the United States*

| Source and date (1) | Peak (2) | Year (3) | Daily rate (*million barrels*) (4) |
|---|---|---|---|
| PMPC, 1951 (a) | X | 1963<br>1975 | ( 7.7)<br>( 5.0) |
|  | X | 1967<br>1975 | ( 8.8)<br>( 7.9) |
|  |  | 1975 | ( 10.0) |
| Egloff, 1951 (b) |  | 1960<br>1975 | ( 8.2)<br>( 12.3) |
| Ayres, 1952 (c) | X | 1960 | (<8.2) |
| Swearingen, 1952 (d) |  | 1967 | 9.0 |
| Ayres, 1955 (e) | X | 1965<br>1975 | ( 8.2)<br>( 5.5) |
| Lasky, 1955 (f) | X | 1960–65<br>1975–? | ( 8.2)<br>(7.5-8.0) |
| Cadle, 1955 (g) |  | 1975 | 11.2 |
| Hubbert, 1956 (h) | X | 1965<br>1975 | ( 7.4)<br>( 5.8) |
|  | X | 1970<br>1975 | ( 8.2)<br>( 7.9) |
| Pogue & Hill, 1956 (i) | X | 1973<br>1975 | ( 9.6)<br>( 8.8) |
| Ion, 1956 (j) |  | 1965<br>1975 | 8.3-9.3<br>8.3-9.3 |
|  | X | 1960–80?<br>1975 | 8.3<br>11.0 |
| AIME, 1956 (k) |  | 1975<br>1975 | 11.2<br>11.1 |
| Hill *et al.*, 1957 (l) | X | 1966<br>1970–80 | 9.5<br>( 11.0) |

For sources see p. 28.

| Source & date | Annual rate (*billion barrels*) (5) | Explicit ultimate reserves (\*) or implied cumulative discoveries through terminal date (col. 3), as of 12/31/56 (*billion barrels*) (6) | Col. 5 as percentage of 1956 production (7) |
|---|---|---|---|
| PMPC, 1951 | 2.8<br>1.8 | } 132 minimum | 108<br>69 |
| | 3.2<br>2.9 | } 141 minimum | 123<br>112 |
| | 3.6 | 150 minimum | 138 |
| Egloff, 1951 | 3.0<br>4.5 | } 1,000\*-2,000\* | 115<br>173 |
| Ayres, 1952 | <3.0 | 100\* | 115 |
| Swearingen, 1952 | (3.3) | 158 minimum | 127 |
| Ayres, 1955 | 3.0<br>2.0 | } 140\* | 115<br>77 |
| Lasky, 1955 | 3.0<br>2.6-2.9 | 150\*<br>250\* | 115<br>100-112 |
| Cadle, 1955 | (4.1) | 160 minimum | 158 |
| Hubbert, 1956 | 2.7<br>2.1 | } 150\* | 104<br>81 |
| | 3.0<br>2.9 | } 200\* | 115<br>112 |
| Pogue & Hill, 1956 | 3.5<br>3.2 | } 165\* | 135<br>123 |
| Ion, 1956 | (3.0-3.7)<br>(3.0-3.7) | 110-120 minimum<br>138-152 minimum | 115-142<br>115-142 |
| | (3.0)<br>(4.0) | 93-152 minimum<br>158 minimum | 115<br>154 |
| AIME, 1956 | (4.1)<br>(4.1) | 160 minimum<br>160 minimum | 158<br>158 |
| Hill *et al.*, 1957 | (3.5)<br>4.0 | } 250\* | 135<br>154 |

## Description of Capacity and Production Estimates

The estimates of future capacity and production are listed chronologically, by the year in which they were made, in column 1 of Table 4. The X's in column 2 indicate whether the author specifies that the figure will be the historical peak of domestic annual crude oil production. Column 3 indicates the year to which each estimate refers. Columns 4 and 5 show all estimates as both a daily and an annual rate of production; the estimate as presented by its author is shown without parentheses. Column 7 shows the estimates, for purposes of

---

SOURCES, TABLE 4:

(a) *Resources for Freedom,* Report of the President's Materials Policy Commission (Washington, D. C.: U. S. Government Printing Office, 1952), I, 108.

(b) G. Egloff, "Oil and Gas as Industrial Raw Materials," *Resources for Freedom,* Report of the President's Materials Policy Commission (Washington, D. C.: U. S. Government Printing Office, 1952), IV, 193.

(c) E. Ayres, "Synthetic Liquid Fuels—When and How?" *Petroleum Processing,* January, 1952, pp. 41-44.

(d) J. E. Swearingen, "Meeting Future Petroleum Demands," *Oil and Gas Journal,* November 17, 1952, pp. 328-36.

(e) E. Ayres, "Energy Resources for the Future," *Oil and Gas Compact Bulletin,* XIV, No. 1 (June, 1955), 20f.

(f) S. G. Lasky, unpublished manuscript.

(g) A. Cadle, "An Appraisal of Future Energy Demand and Supply in the United States," paper presented before American Petroleum Institute Petroleum Industry Buyers, San Francisco, November 15, 1955.

(h) M. K. Hubbert, "Nuclear Energy and the Fossil Fuels," *Drilling and Production Practice—1956* (New York: American Petroleum Institute, 1957 [interpolated from Fig. 21]), p. 17.

(i) J. E. Pogue and K. E. Hill, *Future Growth and Financial Requirements of the World Petroleum Industry* (New York: Chase Manhattan Bank, 1956). Presented at annual meeting of the American Institute of Mining, Metallurgical and Petroleum Engineers, Petroleum Branch, February 21, 1956.

(j) D. C. Ion, "Oil Resources in the Next Half Century," paper presented at Institute of Petroleum Summer Meeting, Torquay, England, June 6-10, 1956.

(k) Production Review Committee, Petroleum Branch, American Institute of Mining and Metallurgical Engineers, *Oil and Gas Development and Production* (Dallas: AIME, Petroleum Branch, February, 1956).

(l) K. E. Hill, H. D. Hammar, and J. G. Winger, "Future Growth of the World Petroleum Industry," paper presented at meeting of American Petroleum Institute Division of Production, Rocky Mountain District, Casper, Wyoming, April 25, 1957.

comparison, on a common basis as a percentage of 1956 production. Column 6 is discussed on p. 33.

Again, the estimates are individually described before they
are discussed. (Unless noted otherwise in the following paragraphs references to the original estimates and the author's
explanation of his estimate can be assumed to be that listed
in Table 4.)

The estimates of the President's Materials Policy Commission are presented in the Commission's report only in graphic
form as "three possible trends in U.S. crude production,"
with no supporting discussion or argument. They are not
considered here to be comparable with other estimates listed
in Table 4, for which there are supporting arguments. In
their original form they were apparently meant to indicate
the range of optimistic, pessimistic, and moderate expectations.

The Egloff estimates in the PMPC report likewise appear
without supporting argument, although it is apparent from
the accompanying highly optimistic reserve estimate (see
pp. 14, 17) that Egloff did not envisage any peaking of output
due to physical limitations during the period considered
herein.

Ayres' 1952 estimate of a peak production of under 3 billion
barrels in 1960 is derived directly from an assumption that
ultimate reserves amount to 100 billion barrels. According to
Ayres, given a total cumulative output for the United States
as a whole and the production record of a considerable fraction of the total producing life, there is, at least in terms of
order of magnitude, a narrow range of possibility for the future course of oil production. With a given ultimate total, the
higher the production peak the sooner it must occur and the
steeper it will be.[21] Ayres further notes that if the date of the
peak proves to be much later than 1960 it must mean that
ultimate reserves are much higher than his assumption. But,

[21] This latter point has also been stressed by M. K. Hubbert (*Proceedings,
United Nations Scientific Conference on Conservation and Utilization of Resources* [New York: United Nations, 1950], I, 104). Note, however, the opposite
assumption in the PMPC figures.

he continues, extrapolations seem to indicate that 100 billion barrels is not too high; and even if reserve estimates were increased by 50 per cent the production peak would be delayed by only a few years. Ayres concludes: "We seem to have a choice between prediction of expansion for the indefinite future, based upon hope, and prediction of the more probable shape of things to come, based upon reason." [22]

The method of treating aggregate national production over time in the same manner as the production of an individual field may be termed the "decline-curve" technique. In the record of any field the production level rises to a peak as the field is developed, then falls as the effect of depletion exerts an ever greater limitation on output. Such a production curve for a single field is called a "decline curve" because it traces the long period of decline subsequent to peak production. By analogy, according to this method, national production should reach a peak and then go into a long period of decline as ultimate reserves are depleted. The area under the decline curve for the entire life of an individual field equals the cumulative production of that field during its lifetime. By the same token, given ultimate reserves for the nation as a whole and the record of production, the decline-curve approach assumes that the curve can be extrapolated to take into account the current trend and at the same time imply a cumulative production equal to ultimate reserves.

In a later article Ayres takes note of 200-billion barrel ultimate-reserve estimates and extrapolates U.S. production to 1993 based on both the 100-billion and 200-billion figures. According to his analysis, a doubling of the reserve total results merely in the postponement of the production peak from 1960 to 1970. If the 200-billion figure is valid, he says, the evidence should become clear by 1960.[23]

In his most recent consideration of the subject, Ayres has raised his estimate of the peak to a flat 3 billion barrels and

[22] E. Ayres, "Synthetic Liquid Fuels—When and How?" *Petroleum Processing,* January, 1952, pp. 41-44.

[23] E. Ayres, "U. S. Oil Outlook: How Coal Fits In," *Coal Age,* LVIII, No. 8 (August, 1953), 70-73.

postponed its occurrence to 1965, with a decline to 2 billion barrels a year by 1975. (See Table 4.) Ayres provides no further details as the basis for this change.

The Swearingen estimate is based on individual forecasts of the productive capacity in 1967 for the five districts into which the Petroleum Administration for Defense divided the United States. The estimate allows for a large secondary production but assumes no drastic technological changes or new secondary recovery methods. His forecasts are, he contends, more than mathematical projections, for they reflect the representative opinion of geologists and geophysicists in the various districts.

Lasky obtains his first estimate (3 billion barrels) from the first derivative of a logistic growth curve fitted to the cumulative record of United States oil production, which is another mathematical way of handling the decline-curve concept. This logistic analysis indicates ultimate cumulative production of 150 billion barrels. The second estimate, ranging from 2.6 to 2.9 billion barrels as the annual rate of production, "is the result of fitting a logistic curve to the annual production series." It indicates a plateau within that range reachable by about 1975; this implies about 250 billion barrels of ultimate cumulative production. Lasky concludes that the point of inflection on the growth curve of cumulative production is as yet indeterminate. He adds that a compromise between the two estimates indicates a flat peak of about 2.8 billion barrels a year annual production persisting over the period 1965–75 before beginning to decline. The implied ultimate cumulative production for this compromise estimate is about 200 billion barrels. The basic assumption of this method, according to Lasky, is that "the past interplay of forces indicates the course of their future interplay." [24]

The Cadle estimate is what the author terms a "guess-estimate" applied to a consideration of the proportions of total energy requirements in the United States that will be supplied from domestic production of the various fuels. "The indica-

[24] Personal communication.

tions are," says Cadle, "that crude oil production in the U.S. will be over 11,000,000 b/d in 1975," or 4.1 billion barrels a year.

Hubbert is a pioneer in the use of the decline-curve approach to estimating future national production. He extrapolates a production curve through time on the basis of the production record to date and an assumption as to the size of ultimate reserves. Taking alternative assumptions of 150 and 200 billion barrels as ultimate reserves, he derives mathematically in the first instance a peak output of 2.7 billion barrels in 1965, in the second a peak output of 3 billion barrels in 1970.

The estimates of Pogue and Hill are based on an analysis of past production trends, proved reserve-production ratios, and discovery rates, which carries their projection through 1965, the course of subsequent years being a decline curve such as used by Hubbert and Ayres. The decline curve in this instance is based on the assumption that approximately one-half of ultimate reserves had been discovered by 1956, implying a total figure of 165 billion barrels for ultimate reserves (see p. 19).

The several estimates by Ion are contained in a paper in which he forecasts world oil demand and supply through 1975. The highest figure among his estimates in Table 4 represents the United States production that would be forthcoming if Middle East oil were for any reason not available. It is therefore closest to the "availability" concept of the present discussion. Ion notes that all the output levels he lists would, however, be possible only because of offshore production in quantity. If Middle East oil is allowed "to play the part it could," United States production, according to Ion, might hit a peak of 8.3 million barrels a day (3 billion barrels a year) within a few years and then hold near that level for about twenty years.

The AIME estimate is derived from two independent sources. The higher figure is based on an estimate by the President's Materials Policy Commission for total Free World output in 1975. The AIME committee resolved this total into United States and foreign production through unspecified calculations. The lower figure was obtained by projecting the trend of recent United States production as calculated by Pogue and Hill (although this was not the basis of the Pogue and Hill projections—see above).

The first estimate by Hill *et al.* is a trend projection based on the assumption of a discovery rate of 3.6 billion barrels per year and a decline in the reserve-production ratio from 11.6 in 1956 to 10.3 by 1966. The second is the peak production indicated by a decline curve drawn on a 250-billion barrel ultimate-reserve basis.

In column 6 of Table 4 the estimates of future production are compared on the basis of implied or explicitly stated reserves. The latter, noted by an asterisk, are the figures for ultimate reserves (referred to by some of the authors as total cumulative production through time) from which the production estimates are derived or with which they are associated. With the remaining estimates, for which no explicit reserve figure is stated, a straight-line growth in production was assumed from 1956 to the terminal year or between intermediate years, if noted, and an allowance of a ratio of 10 between proved reserves and production was made for the terminal year.[25] The straight-line growth and reserve-production ratio are, of course, wholly arbitrary assumptions, and are used solely as a simple means of obtaining, on a uniform basis, some idea of the *minimum* total reserves through time required by the respective production estimates.

In addition to the foregoing primary production-capacity estimates, there is a single estimate of future secondary production by itself. Sweeney has taken Torrey's 1955 estimates of secondary reserves and resources and constructed a decline curve linked to the Pogue and Hill decline curve for primary

[25] Data provided by Swearingen allow the calculation of cumulative total discoveries based on the course of production he specified to the terminal year. The figure in Table 4, column 6, also employs the proved reserve-production ratio of 13 used by Swearingen for that year.

production. "The peak water-flood production was estimated as an approximate 25 per cent of the total production at that time. This point was predicted to occur shortly after the total production had reached a peak when new discoveries would be insufficient to maintain the rate of production. If the present growth of water flood is extrapolated, this peak could be achieved as early as 1965. However, a less optimistic rate of increase was assumed so that this peak was reached in 1980. The total annual production at that time from the curve prepared by Pogue and Hill is 3,000,000 bbl. [*sic*] The peak annual water-flood production is then 750,000,000 bbl." [26]

*Comparison of Capacity-Production Estimates*

Table 5 shows a comparison of 1975 capacity-output estimates and the corresponding ultimate reserves or minimum cumulative discoveries by listing the appropriate figures from columns 5 and 6 of Table 4. The first group of figures in Table 5 consists of estimates of 1975 production or capacity that are accompanied by the expectation of a production peak in the period through 1975. The estimates in the second group do not carry that expectation.[27]

Except for the PMPC estimates, all those in Group I are associated with a specific ultimate-reserve estimate, and the figures for 1975 were obtained by means of the decline-curve approach or its equivalent. The essential difference between the two groups, as expressed in the expectation or non-expectation of a production peak, is the assumption that resources either will or will not exercise a limit to the growth in production (at more or less constant real costs) within the period through 1975.

[26] A. E. Sweeney, Jr., "The Future of Water Flooding in the U. S.," *The Petroleum Engineer,* xxviii, No. 5 (May, 1956), B-82.

[27] The unexplained estimate of Egloff in Table 4 is omitted from Table 5.

Not only is the decline-curve approach utilized by almost all the estimators in the first group, but it is the preponderant basis for all estimates of future oil production. Such popularity seems to be due to the fact that the approach has a seductive simplicity that masks its fundamental fallacies. The simplicity

TABLE 5

## Comparison of 1975 Capacity-Output Estimates and Corresponding Ultimate Reserves or Minimum Cumulative Discoveries

(In billion barrels)

| Source | 1975 figure | Ultimate reserves | Minimum cumulative discoveries |
|---|---|---|---|
| *Group I* | | | |
| Hill *et al.* | 4.0 | 250 | |
| Lasky | 2.6-2.9 | 250 | |
| Hubbert | 2.9 | 200 | |
| Pogue & Hill | 3.2 | 165 | |
| Hubbert | 2.1 | 150 | |
| PMPC | 2.9 | | 141 |
| Ayres | 2.0 | 140 | |
| PMPC | 1.8 | | 132 |
| | | | |
| *Group II* | | | |
| Cadle | 4.1 | | 160 |
| AIME | 4.1 | | 160 |
| Ion | 4.0 | | 158 |
| Ion | 3.0-3.7 | | 138-152 |
| PMPC | 3.6 | | 150 |

*Group I:* Production peak 1975 or earlier.
*Group II:* No production peak expectation by 1975.
SOURCES: See Table 4.

in turn derives from the neatness of its *ex post* application. That is, the production record of an exhausted field, when charted, typically describes a rise to a peak and a subsequent protracted decline to zero. Of course, the nearer a field is to the end of production, the more accurate will be the estimate of total cumulative production (i.e., ultimate reserves, on the aggregate level) and the level of production throughout the remainder of the producing life. But by the same token, the earlier the point of estimation is in the life history of the field, the less accurate will be the assumption as to total cumulative production and the wider the range of possible production for any given year in the future. To put it another way, unless the production cycle has proceeded well toward its end the estimator can never be certain where he stands on the cycle, especially if it is still in the growth phase. This point is well illustrated in Tables 4 and 5 by the wide range of estimates for a given year and by the change of given estimates in the light of a slightly longer production record.

A second major shortcoming of the decline-curve technique is its exclusion of technological change. This is embodied in the assumption of a given magnitude of ultimate reserves, based on the proved-reserve concept, hence current technology. It is paradoxical that the devotees of the decline curve ignore in the basis of their analogy—the curve for the individual field—the abundant evidence that the premise of a unique curve is false. Many fields show two or even more peaks in their production record, the result of secondary recovery or the discovery and exploitation of deeper reservoirs. These events are essentially the application of improved technology. (Ayres even displays such curves and discusses their basis, but denies that this aspect of the analogy can be carried from the individual field to the national aggregate.[28]) An observer of the production record as it climbed to the first peak, however, would falsely conclude from the record that there would be only a single cycle. This is not to argue the likelihood or even possibility of multiple cycles in the aggregate production record, but as noted in the discussion of the reserve-resource esti-

---

[28] E. Ayres and C. A. Scarlott, *Energy Sources—The Wealth of the World* (New York: McGraw-Hill Book Co., 1952), pp. 35 f.

mates, the static treatment of technology is inconsistent with any consideration of the future.

Still another serious shortcoming of the decline-curve technique is the fallacious assumption that on the aggregate level (i.e., in dealing with national production) the resource position is the only significant determinant of production. This ignores the fact that demand, the level of imports, and the relative prices of substitute fuels are actually more important than the resource position in determining the level of production in any year or period such as a decade. This means that even with a given resource position the course of production over time will be influenced by the level of preceding production. For example, a low level of demand (due, for instance, to a decline in economic activity), a high level of imports, or lower prices of substitute fuels in the near future would, even within the internal logic of the decline curve, affect the nature and the timing of the production peak and the period of decline. Thus, with a given resource position the peak could be postponed, it could be higher, and the period of decline longer.

In addition to the conceptual flaws in the decline-curve approach there are also errors in the derivation and use of the curve itself. The curve is often drawn, for example, with perfect symmetry and rounded peak, in seeming confusion with the normal distribution curve; yet the examples of individual fields show that wide variation is possible. The decline curve is, in short, the kind of mechanical extrapolation of statistics which this study seeks to avoid. Indeed, the more rigid mathematical pursuit of the technique employed by some of its proponents implies that the results are more unqualified predictions than forecasts.

The current popularity of the decline curve justifies the emphasis placed here on its shortcomings in principle and in interpretation, although such criticism casts doubts on the usefulness of nearly all the estimates in Group I of Table 5. At the same time, however, with respect to the figures in Group II, it must be recognized that it is all too easy to ignore the possibility of resource limitations and to assume, in effect, infinite reserves. The estimate then refers more to potential demand, given the corresponding availability on the supply side. Some of the estimates in the second group do, perhaps, have such an "infinite reserve" flavor.

The foregoing discussion may seem to suggest that the present study will provide a "better" estimate than any that has been made heretofore. But there is no such thing as a "true" or "correct" estimate of the future. Any of the figures in Tables 1 through 5 could turn out to be the same as those that will develop historically, yet the actual occurrence of such figures could be for reasons quite different from those in the mind of the estimator. As stated in the introduction to this study, the intention of the analysis is not to match a new estimate with existing ones but to build on the latter in the light of considerations that have not, in the opinion of the author, received sufficient acknowledgment or emphasis. The use of the multiplication factor on reserves, for example, is a recognition of technological improvements in recovery that can now be expected, as will be demonstrated. Likewise, in attempting to judge the reasonable expectations with respect to availability in 1975, it is appropriate to examine the indicated significance of technology. Accordingly, technology as a determinant of future domestic crude oil availability is the subject of the following section.

## TECHNOLOGY AS A DETERMINANT OF FUTURE

## DOMESTIC CRUDE OIL AVAILABILITY

### Discovery Technology

It was inferred from current opinion, in column 4 of Table 3, that somewhere between 100 billion and 500 billion barrels of oil remain to be discovered. Unless and until this oil is discovered, however, it might as well not exist. What are the prospects that the bulk of undiscovered oil will in fact be found?

Discussions of future discovery prospects tend to produce a welter of statistics concerning the ratio of successful holes to dry holes, oil discovered per exploratory well, per foot drilled, and the like. Such statistics cannot be wholly ignored, but it is all too easy to become preoccupied with trend projections, instead of focusing on the determinants of the future behavior of the variables. The proved-reserve concept, moreover, again confuses matters, since discovery, when defined in relation to it, includes additions to proved reserves in both known and newly found reservoirs. This in turn makes it difficult to define discovery in relation to time (i.e., oil added to proved reserves in one year may be in a reservoir actually discovered in a previous year). In short, the use of statistical evidence in the manner cited involves an *a priori* assumption of the continuation of present trends and the exclusion of further technological progress.

An example of such use of statistics is found in a recent study which projects the following percentage declines between 1945 and 1965: oil discovered per exploratory well—67 per cent; oil discovered per oil well drilled—50 per cent; oil discovered per foot of hole drilled—67 per cent.[29] The statistical evidence can be recognized, however, without becoming involved in trend projection and detailed data. It is sufficient to observe that according to the evidence, oil is currently becoming more difficult to find, in the sense that more preliminary work is needed to find favorable geologic circumstances, and the average depth of newly found reservoirs is increasing.

To some observers this is in itself an indication of scraping the bottom of the barrel, a warning that the finite limit of actual resources in the ground is being approached. Such argument implies that current technology is approaching the limit

[29] K. E. Hill, H. D. Hammar, and J. G. Winger, "Future Growth of the World Petroleum Industry," paper presented at meeting of American Petroleum Institute Division of Production, Rocky Mountain District, Casper, Wyoming, April 25, 1957.

of human capability to probe all the possible physical loca-
tions of oil under the area of the United States and the adjacent continental shelf—that no oil exists beyond where we may
be tempted to look with present technology. But the possible
relation of discovery rates to resource limitations is at best
tenuous. Discoveries of proved reserves thus far have tended
to increase in proportion with annual production.[30]

On the other hand, the argument is meaningful if stated in
relation to economic and technological circumstances. A declining success level in the search for oil may indicate that
the limit of oil discoverable with current technology at current costs is being approached. But there are strong reasons
for believing that even this is unlikely. In the first place, a
large portion of the area of the United States is geologically
favorable to potential oil production but has not been given
the intensive exploration and development effort of present
and past producing "provinces." In 1951 it was estimated that
this area was some 100 times greater than the area proved productive to date.[31] Of course, this does not mean that the ultimate productive area in the United States will necessarily be
increased by 100-fold, 50-fold, or even 10-fold. It does mean,
however, that there is plenty of room in which to continue
the search for oil with good justification.

Among the relatively unexplored areas, the possibilities of
the continental shelf are generally acknowledged to be extraor-
dinarily good. "A factor which gives added assurance of the
ultimate high productivity of the continental shelf regions is
that throughout most of their extent they consist of and are
a part of the Tertiary sequence of rocks. These . . . have ac-

---

[30] Gonzalez, *op. cit.,* pp. 64-69.

[31] Committee on Oil and Gas Availability, *Petroleum Productive Capacity*
(Washington, D. C.: National Petroleum Council, 1952), pp. 9, 10, 85-93; *cf.* also,
D. D. Moore, *Role of Technology in the Future of Petroleum,* Report by
Battelle Memorial Institute to the President's Materials Policy Commission,
September 15, 1951 (unpublished), p. 10. According to Moore, "the vast bulk
of reserves are in a very few large fields comprising roughly 1,900 square
miles, or only two-tenths of one per cent of the favorable area." There is
some ambiguity, however, as to the proved reserves to which Moore refers.
Slightly more than one-half of reserves are in "giant fields," i.e., those with
ultimate reserves of 100 million barrels or more.

counted for over 60 per cent of all the past petroleum discoveries. They are generally soft rocks, easily folded and deformed into traps, and they are high in organic content. They have suffered less erosion than the older rocks which may account in part for their higher productivity. For reasons such as these, they are much favoured geologically." [32]

At the same time, it is questionable whether the possibilities of known productive areas are being exhausted. According to one claim "there is no evidence that old areas respond to exploratory effort any less than new ones." [33] In any event, there has been failure in the past to explore known structures thoroughly, and there has tended to be a preoccupation with some types of geological traps at the expense of other types. Negative results in one portion of a structure (such as the crest of an anticline) have not always been followed up by tests of the flanks. And if it should develop that about three-quarters of all the oil ultimately found in the United States occurred in stratigraphic traps, as one authority believes may be true,[34] then the opportunities for future exploratory work are large indeed, for approximately three-quarters of all exploratory effort to date has been in the search for structural traps.[35] Even

[32] A. I. Levorsen, "Estimates of Undiscovered Petroleum Reserves," *Proceedings,* United Nations Scientific Conference on the Conservation and Utilization of Resources (New York: United Nations, 1950), I, 97.

According to a recent study of the worldwide occurrence of petroleum, 50 per cent of the world's major oil fields (236 fields, excluding the Soviet bloc, with ultimate reserves of more than 100 million barrels each) are of Tertiary age, and account for 38 per cent of total proved reserves. If the influence of the great Middle East fields is excluded, Tertiary fields account for 50 per cent of the remainder, containing 54 per cent of the reserves. (G. M. Knebel and Guillermo Rodriguez-Eraso, "Habitat of Some Oil," *Bulletin,* American Association of Petroleum Geologists, XL, No. 4 [April, 1956], 557.)

[33] F. J. Gardner, "Dear John, We're Not Running Out of Oil," *Oil and Gas Journal,* April 18, 1955, p. 251.

[34] P. L. Lyons, "Future of Geophysics," *Bulletin,* American Association of Petroleum Geologists, XXXIX, No. 7 (June, 1955), 1210.

[35] A. I. Levorsen, "Geologists Are Talking About . . . ," *The Petroleum Engineer,* XXVIII, No. 2 (February, 1956), B-39 ff.

The habitat study cited in footnote [32] (Knebel and Rodriguez-Eraso, *op. cit.,* pp. 553-55) found that 80 per cent of the oil covered by the study occurs in anticlinal traps, and excluding the Middle East this type of occurrence still accounts for 40 per cent of oil discoveries. By number of fields, 16 per cent are categorized as stratigraphic traps. It is curious in this regard that in known oil country large favorable areas are not adequately explored and drilled.

A third factor in the probability that resource limits are not being approached is that of depth, which presents possibilities in both known and unexplored areas. It was estimated in 1951 that 80 per cent of all producing fields in the United States had deeper possibilities.[36] It has been observed by Cloninger that, theoretically, oil could occur in sandstones down to 65,260 feet below the surface and in limestones down to 51,300 feet. This would make it possible, says Cloninger, given the necessary source rocks and traps, for oil to be found near the bottom of all favorable sedimentary sections in the United States except the San Joaquin-Sacramento Basin in California, which has an estimated depth of 65,000 to 75,000 feet.[37] This observation cannot be taken too literally, for the influence of depth on such factors as permeability, porosity, temperature, and pressure, as well as purely geological aspects of depth, will affect the incidence of oil in the deep environment. Thus Lees holds that:

> The increase in drilling depths now possible must also lead to many deep discoveries, but not in the ratio of increase of depth. For a number of reasons the depths between 10,-000 and 20,000 feet will not be so prolific as were the levels from grass roots to 10,000 feet. In many oil-bearing areas basement rocks are met at lesser depths than 10,000 feet; in deeper levels the productivity per unit volume of pore-space will be less because of surface shrinkage of the crude, and porosity may be somewhat less. Drilling costs to such depths are so much greater that only an expectation of substantial results will justify the costs, and, superimposed on all this, the discovery of deep objectives is immeasurably

---

all the more important stratigraphic fields are in the Western Hemisphere, and most of them in North America. This may, of course, be no more than a reflection of the more intensive exploration in North America. Stratigraphic traps require more effort to locate.

[36] E. Holman, "Oil's Horizons at Mid-Century," *Proceedings*, American Petroleum Institute, XXXI, No. 1 (1951), 34.

[37] J. S. Cloninger, "How Deep Oil or Gas May Be Expected," *World Oil*, May, 1950, p. 60.

more difficult by both geological and geophysical methods, and the clue of seepage is mostly absent.[38]

But the physical possibilities are largely measured against the relatively limited penetration to date. The fact is, we do not really know much about the occurrence of oil at depth. Through 1955 only 247 wells had been drilled below 15,000 feet (see Table 6); and the bulk of known reserves are shallow (see Table 7).

TABLE 6

*Wells below 15,000 Feet Drilled in the*
*United States through 1955*

| Year | Number of deep wells bottomed | Average depth of deep wells drilled (*feet*) | Deepest well drilled to date (*feet*) |
|---|---|---|---|
| 1938 | 1 | 15,004 | 15,004 |
| 1945 | 4 | 15,870 | 16,655 |
| 1946 | 1 | 15,542 | 16,655 |
| 1947 | 8 | 15,891 | 17,823 |
| 1948 | 7 | 16,047 | 17,823 |
| 1949 | 11 | 16,421 | 20,521 |
| 1950 | 5 | 15,713 | 20,521 |
| 1951 | 12 | 15,822 | 20,521 |
| 1952 | 24 | 15,874 | 20,521 |
| 1953 | 34 | 16,127 | 21,482 |
| 1954 | 59 | 15,883 | 21,482 |
| 1955 | 80 | 15,957 | 22,559 |

SOURCE: E. Adams, "80 Wells Completed Below 15,000 Ft. in 1955," *The Petroleum Engineer*, XXVIII, No. 2 (February, 1956), B-21.

The compilers of Table 7 observe: "It is to be expected that the deeper picture will probably improve with time as

[38] G. M. Lees, "Review of Techniques for Oil and Gas Discovery," *Proceedings*, United Nations Scientific Conference on Conservation and Utilization of Resources (New York: United Nations, 1950), III, 5.

more and deeper wildcats are drilled. However, this is the depth habitat of oil as it is known today. There must be some reason for the occurrence of the bulk of our oil, 85 per cent, at depths between 2,000 and 8,000 feet." [39] It would seem that the reason sought for the pattern of depth distribution may be largely supplied by the authors themselves. The pattern is only a reflection of our knowledge today. Until the record of deep drilling has proved otherwise the potential of deeper oil occurrence cannot be arbitrarily minimized.

TABLE 7

### Subsurface Depth of Occurrence of Oil in the Major Oil Fields of the Free World

| Depth range (feet) | Total Free World | | Free World except Middle East | |
|---|---|---|---|---|
| | Per cent of reserves in each depth range | Per cent of fields in each depth range | Per cent of reserves in each depth range | Per cent of fields in each depth range |
| 0– 1,000 | 1.5 | 4.7 | 3.9 | 4.8 |
| 1,000– 2,000 | 6.2 | 9.4 | 13.3 | 9.6 |
| 2,000– 3,000 | 10.2 | 12.9 | 18.0 | 13.1 |
| 3,000– 4,000 | 26.2 | 13.7 | 20.9 | 14.2 |
| 4,000– 5,000 | 16.8 | 13.5 | 10.6 | 13.6 |
| 5,000– 6,000 | 9.5 | 12.1 | 13.6 | 11.5 |
| 6,000– 7,000 | 14.0 | 9.9 | 8.0 | 9.6 |
| 7,000– 8,000 | 8.5 | 7.9 | 5.4 | 7.3 |
| 8,000– 9,000 | 3.5 | 6.3 | 2.5 | 6.2 |
| 9,000–10,000 | 1.6 | 3.5 | 1.7 | 3.7 |
| 10,000–11,000 | 1.5 | 3.8 | 1.3 | 3.8 |
| 11,000–12,000 | 0.4 | 1.8 | 0.4 | 1.9 |
| 12,000 and over | 0.1 | 0.5 | 0.4 | 0.7 |

SOURCE: G. M. Knebel and Guillermo Rodriguez-Eraso, "Habitat of Some Oil," *Bulletin,* American Association of Petroleum Geologists, XL, No. 4 (April, 1956), 560.

[39] Knebel and Rodriguez-Eraso, *op. cit.,* p. 559.

Still another factor is the oil potential in unorthodox sources. Thus, Levorsen argues that full-scale discovery efforts should be made on such currently novel sources as pre-Cambrian and basement rocks, crystalline rocks, volcanics, and continental or fresh-water deposits. All these sources have yielded reservoirs where conditions were favorable; all are present in large volumes and have been tested in relatively few places.[40] Levorsen also points out that Cambrian rocks, in addition, seem to represent almost ideal potential reservoir conditions, nor has it yet been proved that no oil was formed in Cambrian rocks during the Cambrian period. Moreover, many traps do not reach up into younger rocks, hence many Cambrian traps are not yet tested. Levorsen concludes that whether or not the Cambrian are or can be source rocks, their large-scale occurrence, permeability, and many large untested traps offer the "extremely inviting possibility that the Cambrian will become the next great producing system in the U.S. and Canada." [41]

There seems to be no reason to believe, in view of the many unexploited or partially exploited opportunities described above, that discovery will be hampered by approach to the limits of current technology, at least in the period through 1975, although it is possible that further application of this technology cannot be accomplished except at some increase in cost. This raises the question of what advances in the technology of discovery can probably be expected in order to yield still further benefits in additional discoveries without higher costs.

There is general agreement in the industry that spectacular innovations in discovery techniques are improbable; or rather, technological advance will consist of a slow but steady refinement of existing techniques. In the words of one practitioner, "my expectation is that the discovery tools of the future are not likely to be importantly different from those of the present . . . Undoubtedly many refinements and improvements of

---

[40] A. I. Levorsen, "Where Will Tomorrow's Oil Be Found?" *World Oil* April, 1955, pp. 76-81.
[41] *Idem,*

all methods will be made, but no new method or principle of search is remotely in sight at present." [42] Although this statement was made in 1949, no evidence to refute it has developed in subsequent years. Indeed, it can be argued that the most important discovery tool of the future will be the same as that of the past—the drill. Knowledge of the subsurface accumulated through the drilling of dry holes as well as through producers is of much greater significance than possible new discovery techniques.[43]

One avenue of progress is the better integration of geology and geophysics in the study of individual provinces and sedimentary basins.[44] Another is the wider application of new analytic tools in addition to those already utilized. Among such new approaches are micro-photogeology, remapping of surface structure on small contour intervals, stratigraphic correlation by continuous velocity logging and pollen and spore analysis, the magnetic recording of seismic data, and the applied study of regional geologic history.[45] Not all such progress in discovery techniques will yield lower costs, to be sure, but the significant point is that discovery technology, although currently being strained to maintain the necessary pace, is still open-ended with currently foreseen improvements. The reasonable expectation is that future discovery technology will contribute to the finding of oil where present technology is unable to do so.

### Drilling and Production Technology

With the mounting evidence that future production will mean an ever greater number of wells, including those for ex-

[42] Lees, *loc. cit.*

[43] E. B. Noble, *World Oil,* April, 1955, p. 83.

[44] P. R. Schultz, "Oil Discovery Trends," *Bulletin,* American Association of Petroleum Geologists, XXXVII, No. 7 (July, 1953), 1574; and C. S. Shenkel, Jr., "Superposed Geologic Data as an Exploration Tool," paper given at meeting of American Association of Petroleum Geologists, April 25, 1956, Chicago, Illinois.

[45] A. I. Levorsen, "Geologists Are Talking About . . . ," *The Petroleum Engineer,* XXVIII, No. 2 (February, 1956), B-39 ff.

ploration, drilled deeper and under more difficult conditions (such as offshore location), there is increasing pressure on the oil industry to develop better, more efficient, and hence less costly, drilling techniques. Recent important advances have been made with the development of "jet drilling," which utilizes high velocity jet streams of the drilling fluid at the bit head for efficient removal of cuttings; new bit designs for hard formations; and the use of water, gas, or air as the drilling "fluid." [46] These new techniques and equipment have made possible spectacular increases in rate of penetration and have brought consequent drilling economies. With perfection of the new techniques and knowledge of their limitations, their general adoption should aid the drilling of more and deeper wells.

A new approach using conventional equipment that is being adopted on an increasing scale is "slim-hole" drilling. This technique uses smaller-size equipment to provide a smaller diameter hole than is used in conventional practice. Dramatic cost savings have been reported. Although the limitations on slim-hole work are still being defined, it seems apparent that the major benefit of slim holes will be in exploratory rather than development wells. Nevertheless, it is reasonable to expect that the slim-hole technique will be adopted to the limit of its usefulness, with consequent benefits of increased footage and lower cost.

More radical departures from conventional practices, currently in the development stage, are such techniques as "sonic drilling," "percussion drilling," and the "turbodrill." The conventional technique imparts a rotary motion to a drill bit on the end of a string of pipe by rotating the pipe at the surface. When the length of pipe reaches several miles the stresses to which it is subjected are very great, necessitating the use of the highest grade steel. At the same time, the efficiency of energy transmission through the length of pipe falls off seriously due to the high frictional losses down the hole.

[46] D. Ragland, "The Effect of Modern Drilling Technology on Well Cost," *Drilling & Production Practice—1956* (New York: American Petroleum Institute, 1957), pp. 142-45.

All three of the new approaches employ a self-contained unit at the bottom of the hole, thus reducing or eliminating energy losses between the surface and the bottom. Sonic drilling utilizes a transducer just above the drill bit to translate sonic frequencies (about 300 cycles per second) into mechanical vibrations of the drill bit. Experimentation with this technique is currently in progress.[47]

The percussion drill makes use of a reciprocating hammer unit (similar in principle to the pneumatic drill) operated by the circulating drilling mud at the bottom of the hole to drive a conventional bit into the rock. At the same time the bit is rotated at a comparatively slow speed, as in pneumatic drilling. Originally developed for use in excessively hard formations, the method shows promise for more general use. Penetration rates have been increased by 25 to 50 per cent and at the same time bit life has been prolonged by as much as three times.[48] This percussion technique has already reached the licensing stage.

The turbodrill principle also employs a self-contained unit at the bottom of the hole, consisting of the bit and a turbine to rotate it. Fluid circulated through the pipe from the surface supplies the motive force to operate the turbine. The United States oil industry experimented sporadically with the turbodrill for more than thirty years without real success, which is perhaps explained by the lack of real need for its development. In 1956, however, the principle received wide attention because of the introduction of a Russian version of the turbodrill into this country. The glowing claims made for the Russian equipment served to remind the United States industry of the significant possibilities of the turbodrill in the light of future drilling requirements and circumstances. Subsequent developments involving both Russian- and French-designed equipment indicate the early introduction of the method into United States operations. Probable intensification

[47] *Petroleum Week,* December 14, 1956, p. 30.
[48] *The Petroleum Engineer,* xxix, No. 7 (July, 1957), B-32–B-34; also *Petroleum Week,* June 7, 1957, p. 12.

of the pressure for improvement in drilling methods makes it likely that the potentialities of the turbodrill will be thoroughly exploited in this country during the coming two decades,[49] especially since the relative advantage of the turbodrill increases with depth.

There is now being voiced within the industry the sentiment that the efficiency and capability of existing equipment and methods are now being strained to the limit. Radical new approaches are being proposed that would eliminate entirely the conventional derrick and would revolutionize almost every surface operation in drilling.[50] This is significant not as an indication of dramatic developments in the near future but as evidence that the industry will respond, with technological advances, to the greater drilling demands of the coming decades.[51]

A host of special drilling problems are raised by offshore operations, where the chief difficulty is the provision of a base or platform from which to do the drilling. As brought out in the discussion of resources earlier in this study, an important fraction of total resources is believed to lie under the continental shelf—but the shelf extends out to a depth of 600 feet under water. Can the shelf areas be exploited to a sufficient degree to yield significant supply benefits?

The answer would appear to be an almost unqualified "yes." The pace of progress to date in surmounting the obstacles to offshore operations has been truly astounding. Only a few years ago about 100 feet of water seemed to be the foreseeable limit to offshore drilling. Artificial islands, submersible barges, and platforms were thought to be limited to such relatively shallow depths. By 1956, however, mobile platforms were being designed for use in 300 feet of water; and the complete solution of the depth problem is now all but assured with the development of floating rigs that are already being used to obtain

[49] J. A. LeVelle, "An Engineer's Look at Turbine Drilling," *The Petroleum Engineer*, XXVIII, No. 11 (October, 1956), B-39—B-44.

[50] *Petroleum Week*, June 8, 1956, p. 18.

[51] *Cf.* J. A. LeVelle, "New Concepts Spark Drilling Developments," *The Petroleum Engineer*, XXIX, No. 8 (July 15, 1957), B-39 f.

stratigraphic information through such drilling.[52] Again, this is not to say that producing oil fields on the edge of the continental shelf will be a feature of the near future. One can conclude, however, that the full *potential* of the continental shelf petroleum resources is likely to be within reach for exploitation, if economic circumstances call for it.

A detailed study of its drilling costs by one oil company (a study which is believed to correlate well with general industry experience) provides evidence that onshore, at least, technological advances in drilling have been holding the line against the increased costs of drilling at greater depths.[53] Applying the data in Fig. 3 of that study to the average depth of all wells drilled by the industry, the average depth of new wells drilled in 1955 was almost 10 per cent greater than new well depth in 1950, while the average cost of new wells (in constant dollars) rose something like 1.75 per cent.

Deep drilling has yet to exert a significant influence on the average depth of all new wells being drilled, and it is likely that the rate of increase in the average depth of new wells will accelerate in the future as the proportion of deep wells drilled increases. In Ragland's opinion a further increase of 11 per cent in average depth of new wells, reflecting a larger proportion of deep wells, could raise well costs by almost 75 per cent in the absence of continued technological progress. But the greatest benefits of such progress to date, he observes, have accrued at depth. According to Ragland, in the period 1950–1955, in constant dollar terms, "total well costs decreased from 10 per cent for 3,000-foot wells to about 40 per cent for wells in the 15,000-foot depth range." [54] It would be, perhaps, too much to expect that the average depth of new wells can continue to increase indefinitely at little or no increase in cost, but the achievement of technology to date is reasonable ground for assuming, at worst, only a modest cost increase.

Although petroleum production includes several aspects in

52 *Petroleum Week*, March 16, 1956, p. 19; October 5, 1956, pp. 24 f.
53 Ragland, *op. cit.*, pp. 146 f.
54 *Ibid.*, p. 147.

addition to drilling, the only other aspect of real significance in the present context is recovery. The currently mounting discovery difficulties and costs have caused the oil industry to give great attention in recent years to possibilities of increased recovery. The known secondary resources carry no discovery costs, and increased recovery from future oil discoveries would lower the discovery costs per unit of oil production. The accumulation of knowledge by the industry in its production activities has gradually given it an understanding of the physical nature of underground oil reservoirs and of the forces present in those reservoirs. "Reservoir engineering" has spurred the trend toward operation of a reservoir as a unit, making possible maximum utilization of the energy within the reservoir to produce oil at the surface. The maintenance of reservoir pressure is now a common practice, and in the postwar period there has been a very rapid growth of water injection projects to drive the oil out of the reservoir rock. Along with these developments has come the establishment of state conservation bodies to encourage and even enforce such practices.

Even with current techniques the expected recovery ranges from 60 to 80 per cent for water drive and 30 to 80 per cent for gas drive.[55] Current research and development on the latter score indicate, moreover, that the use of "enriched gas" for injection (i.e., gas containing the added components ethane, propane, and butane in proper proportions) can, under appropriate conditions, give total recovery.[56] Other work on recovery methods involves solvent extraction, the use of detergents to "wash" the oil from the reservoir, and "thermal recovery" of highly viscous oil through *in situ* combustion of a small portion of the oil.

Torrey has estimated that as of January 1, 1956, a total of

[55] R. C. Craze and S. E. Buckley, "The Development and Control of Oil Reservoirs," *Drilling and Production Practice—1943* (New York: American Petroleum Institute, 1944).

[56] N. J. Clark, W. P. Schultz, and H. M. Shearin, "New Injection Method Affords Total Oil Recovery," *The Petroleum Engineer*, xxviii, No. 11 (October, 1956), B-45—B-51.

194 billion barrels of oil was known to exist but was currently unrecoverable.[57] The new techniques now in sight would, of course, be applicable not only to these known resources but also to the indeterminate secondary portion of the 200-300 billion barrels of undiscovered oil included in the resource base estimate made earlier in this study. But the most significant portion of secondary resources is the 194 billion barrels already known to exist. Although future discoveries should contribute to secondary resources that could be exploited in the period through 1975, it is the known resources that can sustain a rapid exploitation of new secondary recovery techniques and which could contribute an explosive boost to total yearly crude oil production.

Expert opinion can be found on both sides of the question of whether the possibilities of increased recovery favor a rapid expansion in output. One of the trade journals, for example, makes the following comments on the condensing gas drive, critical displacement technique, in the same issue that carries an enthusiastic description of it:

> There will be limitations, to be sure. In most instances, . . . propane and ethane will be required to make up the critical composition of injected gas . . . and, this mixture will vary from reservoir to reservoir. Availability of propane and ethane in adequate quantities will be a controlling factor . . . which means that the oil field must be located in an area where ample supplies of these vital hydrocarbons are available at an economic advantage. . . .
> It is not likely that all this will transpire overnight, but will require costly experimentation in both the laboratory and field, as well as take considerable time for individual reservoir study to select the best prospects. Waterflooding took a mighty long time to find widespread application. No doubt, the condensing gas drive process, too, will be around for some time before it is as well known as waterflooding is today.[58]

[57] P. D. Torrey, "Evaluation of U. S. Oil Resources as of January 1, 1956," *Producers Monthly*, June, 1956, pp. 26, 28.
[58] *The Petroleum Engineer*, XXVIII, No. 11 (October, 1956), B-45.

Hubbert also foresees a rise in the recovery level but contends that this could not yield results of much importance. "Because of the slowness of the secondary recovery process . . . it appears unlikely that any improvement that can be made within the next 10 or 15 years can have any significant effect" upon the historical peak of production. The more likely result, he thinks, will be to reduce the rate of decline after culmination of production at the peaks he projects (see p. 32).[59] Similarly, Hill *et al.* note that such advancements in technique as pressure maintenance and secondary recovery methods "tend chiefly to arrest production decline rather than increase output." [60]

On the other hand, the secondary-reserve estimates given in Table 1 show considerable optimism regarding secondary prospects, and articles by industry experts are beginning to carry allusions to the large possibilities of increased recovery that are now opening up. The experts (perhaps because they are experts) do not exhibit the temerity of the present study in essaying a quantitative estimate of these possibilities; but Pratt, for example, observes that "the industry is not content to continue to leave 60 per cent [assuming 40 per cent recovery] . . . of its oil in the ground. The reward for more efficient recovery is too great . . . Much greater recoveries are certain to be achieved." [61] And Gonzalez comments that "unitization and pressure maintenance projects and other significant new developments may mean much higher rates of recovery in future than in the past." [62] Finally, Torrey, the outstanding authority on secondary recovery, observes: "A realistic appraisal of the effect of improved recovery technology might be that sufficient additional oil will be produced by this means during

[59] M. K. Hubbert, "Nuclear Energy and the Fossil Fuels," *Drilling and Production Practice—1956* (New York: American Petroleum Institute, 1957), p. 18.
[60] Hill *et al., op. cit.*
[61] W. E. Pratt, "A Geologist's Long-Term Forecast of Petroleum Supply," paper given before Pacific Section, American Association of Petroleum Geologists, Los Angeles, November 9, 1956.
[62] Gonzalez, *op. cit.*, p. 66.

the next 20 years to *in large measure* supplement the anticipated increased demand." [63] (italics added.)

In adopting the view of the optimists among the experts,
certain specific points can be made in argument against the
opposing views that have been cited. To answer the quotation
from *The Petroleum Engineer* (see p. 52), there are certain
differences between the circumstances surrounding the growth
of waterflooding and those in which the new techniques can
be expected to develop. The full benefits of waterflooding are
coming through the advanced state of knowledge of reservoir engineering. The technological environment for the new
methods is thus far more favorable at the initial stage; they
can be developed more rapidly, given sufficient stimulus. Such
stimulus will arise from the pressures on the oil industry to
keep pace with a demand that is already large and gives evidence of growing in the future at an accelerating pace. Because of the constantly larger magnitudes involved, there is a
much stronger incentive to develop and apply new techniques than was true with the currently established ones in
the past. If a given effort expended on secondary recovery
will yield greater, more certain, and quicker results than the
same effort devoted to discovery, it can be expected that the
oil industry will pursue this advantage on a large scale.[64]
And, what may be most important, the 194 billion barrels
of oil in the ground offers attractive cost advantages. Secondary oil is, of course, not free, but the cost of secondary operations must be measured against the costs of discovering new
oil. Even with equivalent costs, the absence of the discovery
risk in secondary oil should certainly tip the balance.

Hubbert's argument concerns the possible magnitude and
pace of the secondary operations themselves rather than the
development of techniques. But the secondary recovery process

[63] P. D. Torrey, "Oil Resources of the United States," *The Oil and Gas Compact Bulletin*, XIV, No. 1 (June, 1955), 49.

[64] See *Petroleum Week*, September 13, 1957, pp. 48 f. There are already independent operators who specialize in buying up producing fields and applying secondary-production methods. (See *Petroleum Week*, August 30, 1957,
p. 21.)

is not slow, as he contends. On the contrary it is much more rapid than that of primary recovery. Most secondary projects have a life of eight to twelve years, whereas the regulated primary production from many existing fields is over a period from five to ten times longer.[65] Indeed, the very decline curves cited by Hubbert show the high peak output attainable shortly after the application of secondary recovery techniques to a given reservoir. Even if production restrictions were extended to secondary operations, the total effect of a widespread simultaneous adoption of a new high-recovery technique could be very large. The total additions to production from hundreds or thousands of individual secondary operations could have a highly significant effect, over a short period, on total output. Such would be the case if there were an industry rush to take advantage of a highly profitable new technique, and the indications do point to the imminent occurrence of a sudden, large jump in the recovery factor. A doubling, for example, is wholly plausible. A recovery factor of two-thirds as the average for the United States within the next fifteen years or so would be well within the possibilities currently being opened up.[66]

## CONCLUSIONS ON DOMESTIC

## CRUDE OIL AVAILABILITY

Before presenting the conclusions of this study on domestic crude oil availability in 1975 it is worth repeating the state-

[65] P. D. Torrey, personal communication.

[66] See M. B. Spangler, *New Technology and the Supply of Petroleum*, Research Paper No. 2 (Chicago: University of Chicago Program of Education and Research in Planning, 1956), Chap. VIII, for an unusual discussion of future progress in recovery. Spangler concludes that the most probable recovery level in 1975 will be 70 per cent. Although the conclusion is preceded by an elaborate but meaningless probability analysis presented in obscure terminology, it is in essence a judgment based on an interesting and useful survey of technological possibilities.

ment made in the introduction: the purpose of the study is not to make projections or forecasts of actual production. The discussion, moreover, is not a technical analysis, offering new basic data from which original estimates can be derived. The conclusions are rather a distillation of expert, technical opinion as interpreted in the light of the concepts and assumptions introduced herein.

The following paragraphs present the conclusions on primary and secondary availability separately. Again, it must be observed that supply is not being matched against a given demand. The indicated availability levels may therefore look startlingly high, but they represent, in the opinion of the author and in the light of the foregoing discussion, reasonable expectations as to the quantity of crude oil that *could* be forthcoming in 1975 from both primary and secondary operations, at no appreciable increase in constant dollar costs.

*Primary Availability*

The two major conclusions concerning primary availability that can be drawn from the preceding discussion are: (a) the magnitude of United States crude oil resources at current costs is such that there should be no resource limitation on continued growth in primary capacity in the period through 1975, and (b) it can be expected that technology will continue to expand the possibilities of probing the environment of oil occurrence so that continued growth in primary capacity can be sustained.

On the basis of these conclusions a quantitative estimate of primary crude oil availability in 1975 may be adopted from among existing expert opinion as being representative of the conclusions. The first conclusion eliminates from consideration the first group of estimates in Table 5, since their basic assumption of a peak in output before 1975 is incompatible with that conclusion. The second conclusion places

the author among the optimists on future oil discovery prospects. The estimates in the second group of figures in Table
5, which are not based on a resource limiting assumption,
range between 3.0 and 4.1 billion barrels as the production
or capacity in 1975. Of these, the Cadle estimate of 4.0 billion and the high estimate of Ion, of 4.1 billion barrels, appear to approximate the conclusions reached herein. (The
AIME estimate is not a truly independent one but is based
on PMPC and Pogue and Hill estimates.) Accordingly, it is
concluded that domestic crude oil availability in 1975 could
be as high as 4.0 billion barrels, in round numbers. If production attained that level in that year it would represent a
54 per cent increase over the 1956 level.

Again, it should be noted that the choice of a figure equivalent to Cadle's estimate and approximating one by Ion does
not mean that these are considered the "best" estimates. Indeed, it will be recalled that Cadle himself describes his
figure as a "guess-estimate," and he does not present any
systematic justification of it. The Ion and Cadle figures are,
however, most consonant with the conclusions stated above,
and best express the judgment of the present study.


## Secondary Availability

The conclusion to be drawn from the discussion of secondary recovery technology is that we are about to enter a period
of explosive growth in such recovery. There exists a wide
technological opportunity, there is the incentive to exploit
that opportunity, and it is likely that there will be a general
movement to do so. For these reasons it is believed that the
pace of development and use of the new, high recovery techniques will be rapid, and the level of secondary production
in 1975 could be very large compared with the present.

An attempt to quantify these expectations in an estimate
of secondary availability in 1975 is more difficult than was
true for primary availability. There is, to begin with, no

collection of expert estimates upon which to base a judgment in the light of the perspective developed herein. Sweeney's secondary-production estimate (see p. 33) is clearly minimal. It is linked with the restrictive Pogue and Hill decline curve for primary output; it is based on secondary reserve-resource estimates by Torrey since superseded by larger ones by the same author; and the estimate is itself a product of the decline curve technique, with its static treatment of technology, the most crucial element in the future of secondary production.

The derivation of an independent estimate of 1975 secondary availability is hampered by the lack of statistics on past and current secondary output. Such statistics are not compiled, but there are available figures for total production from fluid injection operations. In 1953 this output totaled 425 million barrels, and it is estimated that the purely secondary output in that year amounted to some 117 million barrels.[67]

In the absence of any systematic means of arriving at an estimate of 1975 availability, a figure of two billion barrels is chosen to indicate the general magnitude by which total annual crude output could be increased by 1975 at no increase in constant dollar costs. The range of error in this estimate is obviously very great, but if the preceding arguments are accepted, the estimate appears to be, if anything, on the conservative side. It should be noted again that this is not a prediction of two billion barrels of secondary production in 1975; it is a judgment as to what *could* be produced if present circumstances and forces continue to evolve throughout the intervening period as they currently appear to be doing.

The conclusion of this study, therefore, is that the indicated total domestic availability of crude oil in the United States in 1975, at no appreciable increase in constant dollar costs, is on the order of six billion barrels.

[67] A. E. Sweeney, Jr., "The Magnitude of Fluid Injection Operations in the U. S.," *The Petroleum Engineer*, XXVIII, No. 2 (February, 1956), B-120, B-125, B-126.

## OTHER SOURCES OF SUPPLY

*Imports*

Although the preceding discussion has been concerned solely with domestic crude availability, it is not meant to carry the implication that domestic crude output would in that year meet, at no increase in costs, whatever demand may be expected. On the contrary, it can be assumed that imports would also contribute to total supply. Not only should Canada and Venezuela continue to have exportable surpluses available to this country throughout the period to 1975, but there also exist the resources of the Middle East. The known potential capacity of the latter region alone is so enormous [68] that given normal world trade relations and a modicum of political stability in that area, no reasonably projected world demand on that capacity in the period through 1975 could reach the level at which resource limitations would come into play. All this oil constitutes a large reservoir that can be tapped, at lower costs than domestic oil, to the extent that will be determined by world supply-demand relationships, United States import policy, and other factors that are beyond the scope of this study.

Inextricably related to the role of imports in total supply is the matter of price. To a large extent the two are inter-determinate, but there is a substitute source of domestic supply that appears likely to put a ceiling on the possible domestic price level of crude oil. The significance of this possibility is sufficient to warrant additional consideration.

[68] Pratt estimates the *proved reserves* of the Middle East at 230 billion barrels as of the end of 1954. (Joint Committee on Atomic Energy, *op. cit.*, II, 93.)

*Shale Oil*

The substitute source for domestic supply is shale oil, a material obtained from a type of rock known as "oil shale." [69] This rock contains a variable proportion of hydrocarbon material that can be separated from the rock and produced in liquid form as shale oil. The shale oil, in turn, can be hydrogenated and processed by conventional oil refinery practices to yield the same products as petroleum.

Rocks that can be termed oil shales occur in Colorado, Utah, and Wyoming and underlie a large portion of the area between the Appalachians and the Mississippi. The total shale oil content of these rocks is not yet possible to estimate, but the Geological Survey estimates that the shale oil resources of Colorado alone total about 900 billion barrels, including only rock that would yield at least 15 gallons of oil per ton.[70] The richest beds constitute a section up to 90 feet thick assaying 30 gallons to the ton, which alone contain an estimated 126 billion barrels of shale oil,[71] of which 100 billion barrels seem currently recoverable.[72]

It is thus evident that the shale oil resources of the United States constitute an abundant potential domestic source of liquid fuels that is considerably larger than the estimated crude oil resource base. The significance of these resources, which do not involve future discovery and which can be measured, as resources, with much greater accuracy than petroleum resources, has been apparent for some time to both industry and government. Between 1944 and 1956 the Bureau of Mines carried on extensive experimentation which in-

[69] Other domestic sources of liquid fuels, present or potential, such as gilsonite and oil sands, are excluded from consideration because of the limited scale of output they could support.

[70] *Petroleum Week,* February 10, 1956, p. 13.

[71] U. S. Department of Interior, Bureau of Mines, *Synthetic Liquid Fuels, Annual Report of the Secretary of the Interior for 1955,* Part II, "Oil From Oil Shale" (Report of Investigations 5237), July, 1956, p. 3.

[72] S. Klosky, "Oil Shale," *Mineral Facts and Problems,* Bulletin 556, Bureau of Mines (Washington, D. C.: U. S. Department of Interior, 1956), p. 582.

cluded the operation of an oil shale mine and several shale oil pilot plants. The technical feasibility of shale oil recovery was proved beyond question by this work. In addition, investigations by private companies have been under way for the past few years, progressing through the operation of two pilot plants in 1957.

Both geography and the indicated future supply-demand situation on the Pacific Coast, particularly in Southern California, point to that area as the most logical initial market for shale oil. For this reason cost estimates to date have referred to the cost of gasoline from shale oil produced for the Southern California market. These estimates are listed in Table 8.

The three Bureau of Mines estimates of 1952 are taken from a study of a hypothetical operation in which partly processed shale oil is delivered by a 700-mile pipeline to a refinery in the Los Angeles area. The first estimate is for regular-grade gasoline obtained through thermal cracking. The other two are for both regular and premium grades obtained through mild hydrogenation. This study was reviewed in detail by the National Petroleum Council, which concluded that the Bureau of Mines had not been sufficiently conservative in its detailed cost assumptions for the operation as a whole, and offered its own, higher estimates on what it considered to be a more realistic basis. The Bureau of Mines subsequently modified the NPC estimates in turn on the basis of further technological progress in oil shale mining and shale oil processing, although it apparently did not take into account increases in the general price level after 1950. In its most recent reference to the subject, the Bureau of Mines has noted that with a 6 per cent return on investment, the application of the oil industry's percentage depletion rate of 27.5 per cent to the oil shale industry would result in a reduction of as much as 0.9¢ per gallon from shale oil.[73] The most recent estimate is a statement by an official of an oil company currently engaged in pilot-plant and demonstration

[73] U. S. Department of Interior, Bureau of Mines, *op. cit.*, p. 45.

TABLE 8

## Estimates of the Cost of Gasoline from Shale Oil in Southern California

| Source and date | Gasoline cost (cents per gal.) | Remarks |
|---|---|---|
| Bureau of Mines (a), July 1952 | 12 | 250,000 bbl/day capacity, multi-plant shale operation. Full allowance for by-products. 8.4 per cent capital return. |
| | 12 (reg.) 13 (prem.) | 250,000 bbl/day capacity, multi-plant shale operation. Full allowance for by-products. 11.2 per cent capital return. |
| Nat. Pet. Council (b), February 1953 | 16.2 | 39,700 bbl/day refinery in Los Angeles. Costs as of January 1951. |
| | 14.7 | 201,330 bbl/day multi-plant operation. Los Angeles. Costs as of January 1951. |
| Bureau of Mines (c), March 1955 | 11.1 | Modification of National Petroleum Council estimate on basis of subsequent technological progress. |
| Linden (d), February 1956 | 13.0 | Indicated possibility of Union Oil Company pilot project. |

SOURCES:

(a) U. S. Department of Interior, Bureau of Mines, *Synthetic Liquid Fuels, Annual Report of the Secretary of the Interior for 1951*, Part II, *Oil From Oil Shale* (Report of Investigations 4866), July, 1952, pp. 53-54.

(b) National Petroleum Council, *Final Report of Committee on Synthetic Liquid Fuels Production Costs* (Washington, D. C., February 26, 1953), p. 8.

(c) U. S. Department of Interior, Bureau of Mines, *Synthetic Liquid Fuels, Annual Report of the Secretary of the Interior for 1954*, Part II, *Oil From Oil Shale* (Report of Investigations 5119), March, 1955, p. 67.

(d) Herbert E. Linden, President, Oil Shale Corporation, as reported in *Petroleum Week*, February 10, 1956, p. 31.

work. He considers the 13¢ figure quoted in Table 8 to be currently competitive with gasoline from petroleum.[74]

The latest indications are, however, that assessment of the

[74] *Petroleum Week*, February 10, 1956, p. 31.

economics of shale oil operation on the basis of the gasoline product may be misleading. The United States Navy, which has oil shale holdings of its own, now considers that the true significance of shale oil is as a source of jet and diesel fuels, with gasoline as a byproduct,[75] but no cost analyses on this basis have been published.

The true competitive position of this supply source will not be known until the first commercial plants are in operation. If current indications are correct, however, and shale oil is already marginal, a significant price rise in crude oil would be a powerful stimulus in developing the new industry. Shale oil would be meeting crude at a higher price, but shale oil costs would be no greater, thus attracting capital from the petroleum industry to shale oil development. Again, industry costs at various levels of capacity (i.e., ten thousand versus one million barrels a day) can only be guessed at now, but it is obvious that the greater the increase in the price of crude the stronger the stimulus for shale oil expansion. And at some point, at least in theory, a sufficiently high price for crude would enable the shale oil industry to effectively supplant the petroleum industry. Nor should it be overlooked that the costs of shale oil should go down, not up as the benefits of operating experience are applied.

[75] *Petroleum Week,* February 22, 1957, p. 75.

# II

# natural gas

The future of natural gas is a difficult subject because of peculiarities in natural gas occurrence and production. Data from which to infer the magnitude of unknown resources and the various components of future supply are even more scanty than is similar information for petroleum. The assumptions required are therefore less well founded, and it is not surprising to find relatively few public discussions and estimates concerning the subject.

Natural gas has two major modes of occurrence: it is often found by itself, in distinct gas reservoirs, and it can occur together with crude oil. Because the effect of these purely physical circumstances on production characteristics is important, the American Gas Association distinguishes two types of gas occurrence on the basis of production characteristics:

*Non-associated gas* is free gas not in contact with crude oil in the reservoir; and free gas in contact with oil where the production of such gas is not significantly affected by the production of crude oil.

*Associated gas* is free gas in contact with crude oil in the reservoir where the production of such gas is significantly affected by the production of crude oil.[1]

[1] Definitions adopted by the Natural Gas Reserves Committee of the American Gas Association, 1957.

Associated gas constitutes either a "gas cap" overlying the crude oil in the underground reservoir, or gas dissolved in the crude oil, held in solution by the reservoir pressure. This *dissolved gas* is liberated when the pressure is reduced either at the surface or in the sub-surface, when the reservoir pressure drops below the saturation pressure because of withdrawals. To date, non-associated gas has been the most important mode of occurrence; it currently constitutes about two-thirds of total proved reserves of natural gas, with the other two types accounting for roughly equal portions of the remainder.

The various published estimates and opinions concerning future reserves and production of natural gas are examined in the following sections in the same manner as were the oil estimates. Additional features of occurrence, discovery, and production peculiar to natural gas as compared with crude oil are brought into the discussion where relevant. Again, only the literature for the past few years has been surveyed, in order to restrict the discussion to current opinion.

## ESTIMATES OF RESERVES

### Measurement and Definitions

The proved-reserve concept used for oil is also applied to natural gas in the estimation by industry of its reserves: "Proved recoverable reserves of natural gas are those reserves estimated to be producible under present operating practices, with no consideration being given to their ultimate use." [2] But, as is true of oil, there are the same uncertainties and ambiguities to be resolved in deciding whether a known gas occurrence is sufficiently well defined to be so included, and

[2] Natural Gas Reserves Committee of the American Gas Association, *1957 Report.*

the recovery factor must also be taken into account since there are both physical and economic limits to the proportion of the gas in place that can be currently recovered.

One of these limits concerns the pressure at which a gas field is likely to be abandoned. Gas can be forced or pulled to the surface, but ordinarily reaches the surface with the naturally existing pressure in the underground reservoir. This pressure is often very high—thousands of pounds per square inch—and the problem is then the reduction of pressure to a level that can be economically handled in the gathering system. On the other hand, as gas is removed from the reservoir the pressure drops, and there exists for each field a pressure differential (between the reservoir and the gathering pipeline system) at which further operation would be uneconomic. At this point the field must be abandoned. Usually this pressure is rather low and, as noted, can even be negative, but in certain instances abandonment pressures as high as 300 to 500 pounds per square inch are the cutoff point beyond which the gas is considered "unrecoverable." [3]

There is, in addition, the problem of the inclusion in the proved-reserve estimate of individual small gas fields. Many of these are excluded from the estimates on the grounds that it would be impracticable to consider them and that the quantities involved are insignificant relative to the total. The errors inherent in any estimation of natural resources are, of course, very large—so large, in fact, that they probably override errors peculiar to natural gas. This discussion does not use the gas industry's proved-reserve estimates as such, although they are included in total future supply estimates and, are employed in examining certain relationships between natural gas and crude oil.

Future reserves of natural gas cannot be considered in terms of total cumulative reserves through time, as was possible with oil. This is due to the lack of knowledge as to the

[3] J. R. Stockton, R. C. Henshaw, Jr., and R. W. Graves, *Economics of Natural Gas in Texas* (Austin: Bureau of Business Research, University of Texas, 1952), p. 120.

total past "production" of gas, defining "production" to include waste through "venting" (escape of gas without burning), and "flaring" (escape with burning). In the earlier decades of the oil industry an unknown but undoubtedly very large amount of gas was wasted through ignorance, carelessness, and the lack of economic incentive to do otherwise. Until modern technology made pipeline construction economically feasible there was at best a limited market for the gas, which consequently had little or no value. Since the waste was probably a substantial proportion of total past "production," estimates of that production, or of total discoveries to date, are of little use in the present context. This has not prevented some writers on the subject from making an assumption as to the magnitude of total past losses and so constructing an estimate of cumulative discoveries, or reserves to date. Most estimates of ultimate reserves of natural gas, as that term is defined in the preceding discussion of oil, have been made, however, in terms of the "total future supply," which consists of current proved reserves plus anticipated future discoveries of such reserves.

## Description of Estimates

Table 9 lists the current estimates of the "total future supply" of natural gas in the United States. The estimates are reduced to a common basis in column 4 of the table, where proved reserves as of January 1, 1957 have been subtracted from the total future supply estimate in column 2. Column 5 gives an indication of the relative magnitude of each estimate through the ratio between it and 1956 production. (Unless otherwise stated, references for the following descriptions of the estimates are the same as those given in Table 9.)

Terry's 1950 estimate was based on Weeks' estimate of "onshore" oil reserves (see discussion p. 12). Terry estimated that the ratio of gas discoveries to oil discoveries in the future

TABLE 9

## Estimates of Total Recoverable Reserves of Natural Gas in the United States

(In trillion cubic feet)

| Source and date (1) | Estimated total future supply (2) | To be discovered (as of time of estimate) (3) | (as of 1/1/57) (4) | Ratio of total future supply to 1956 production (5) |
|---|---|---|---|---|
| Terry, 1950 (a) | >510 | >330 | >272 | >46 |
| Hinson, 1954 (b) | 586 | 375 | 348 | 53 |
| Interior Dept., 1956 (c) | 875 | 663 | 637 | 80 |
| Pratt, 1956 (d) | 725 | 513 | 487 | 66 |
| Pogue & Hill, 1956 (e) | 570 | 358 | 332 | 52 |
| Hubbert, 1956 (f) | 735 | 511 | 497 | 67 |
| Terry & Winger, 1957 (g) | >1,200 | >984 | >984 | >110 |

SOURCES:

(a) L. F. Terry, "The Future Supply of Natural Gas," *Proceedings*, American Gas Association, 1950, pp. 155-59.

(b) H. H. Hinson, "What's the Present Picture for Natural Gas Reserves?" Report presented before the American Gas Association Financial Forum, October 8, 1954.

(c) Joint Committee on Atomic Energy, *Peaceful Uses of Atomic Energy*, Report of the Panel on the Impact of Peaceful Uses of Atomic Energy (Washington, D. C.: U. S. Government Printing Office, January, 1956), II, 83.

(d) W. E. Pratt, *ibid.*, II, 94.

(e) J. E. Pogue and K. E. Hill, *Future Growth and Financial Requirements of the World Petroleum Industry* (New York: Chase Manhattan Bank, 1956). Presented at annual meeting of the American Institute of Mining, Metallurgical and Petroleum Engineers, Petroleum Branch, February 21, 1956.

(f) M. K. Hubbert, "Nuclear Energy and the Fossil Fuels," *Drilling and Production Practice—1956* (New York: American Petroleum Institute, 1957), p. 15.

(g) L. F. Terry and J. G. Winger, "Sees 1,200 Trillion of U. S. Recoverable Gas," *American Gas Association Monthly*, XXXIX, Nos. 7-8 (July-August, 1957), 10 ff.

should run about 6,000 cubic feet of gas per barrel of oil, hence Weeks' figure should result in 280 trillion cubic feet of onshore gas discoveries.[4] (The gas-oil ratio is discussed in detail below.) To this figure Terry added an arbitrary estimate of 50 trillion cubic feet for offshore gas discoveries, which together with the then proved-reserve level of 180 trillion cubic feet yielded a total future supply of 510 trillion cubic feet. Terry used his gas-oil ratio as a compromise between the then current ratios of 4.1 thousand cubic feet (Mcf) per barrel in gas and oil production and 7.3 Mcf per barrel in proved reserves. He considered that the 6,000-cubic-foot figure was actually conservative, and that his future supply figure of 510 trillion cubic feet should be regarded as a minimum.

Hinson's estimate is based on a gas-oil ratio of 5,000 cubic feet per barrel applied to a somewhat larger (but unspecified) oil reserve estimate than the Weeks figure employed by Terry.

The Department of Interior estimate is contained in its report on the impact of the peaceful uses of atomic energy on the natural gas industry which it made to the McKinney Panel. The report first cites Terry's estimate, noting that his gas-oil ratio "has turned out to be too low." "Considering that it has been necessary in the past to increase both the estimate of ultimate oil reserves and the ratio of gas to oil discoveries," the report continues, "and taking into account the trend toward deeper and deeper drilling, it is likely that larger and larger reserves of natural gas will continue to be found. Thus, a considerable upward adjustment of the Terry estimate is now required." [5] The Department thinks that this adjustment should be by at least a factor of two.

But the Department mistakenly interprets Terry's original

[4] Weeks estimated ultimate oil reserves at 110 billion barrels, leaving 46.5 billion barrels to be discovered as of January 1, 1950. 6,000 $\times$ 46.5 billion equals 279 trillion.

[5] Joint Committee on Atomic Energy, *Peaceful Uses of Atomic Energy*, Report of the Panel on the Impact of the Peaceful Uses of Atomic Energy (Washington, D. C.: U. S. Government Printing Office, January, 1956), II, 83.

estimate to be "ultimate gas reserves," and so terms it. The doubling of Terry's figure to a level of 1,000 trillion cubic feet is the Interior Department's revised estimate of "ultimate gas reserves." In Table 9 this is adjusted to an equivalent total future supply figure.

The Pratt estimate was also presented in a report to the McKinney Panel, in which Pratt voiced the industry consensus as to future developments but emphasized that the actual estimates were his own. Pratt uses a gas-oil ratio of 5 Mcf per barrel, applied to an estimate of total liquid hydrocarbon reserves (i.e., including natural gas liquids, which are discussed later). Pratt implies conservatism in his estimate by citing the fact that outside the United States the ratio is 4 Mcf per barrel of oil, against the current 6–7 Mcf in this country.[6]

The Pogue and Hill estimate is presented as their basis for deriving the trend of future production, with no supporting statements or analysis.

Hubbert's gas estimate is based on his estimate of 150 billion barrels as the ultimate oil reserves of the United States (see discussion of Table 1) which, as of January 1, 1956, left 97.5 billion barrels to be produced. "Then, if we use the gas-oil ratio of current production, we obtain 410 trillion cubic feet of gas as the future reserve. If we assume the ratio of 7,500 cubic feet per barrel, obtained from proved reserves, we obtain a future reserve of 730 trillion cubic feet . . . Of these figures the latter appears the more reliable since the reserves represent a much larger sample than the annual production." [7] For his own use Hubbert adopted the Pratt estimate, as a round number with which his own estimate is in substantial agreement.

The Terry and Winger estimate is based on their colleagues' estimate of ultimate oil reserves of 250 billion barrels. (See Table 1.) Deducting 86 billion barrels of cumula-

---

[6] *Ibid.*, p. 94.

[7] M. K. Hubbert, "Nuclear Energy and the Fossil Fuels," *Drilling and Production Practice—1956* (New York: American Petroleum Institute, 1957), p. 15.

tive discoveries, Terry and Winger apply a gas-oil ratio of 6 Mcf per barrel to the 164 billion barrels of oil remaining to be discovered. This yields indicated future gas discoveries of 984 trillion cubic feet, to which are added 238 trillion of current proved reserves for a total future gas supply of about 1,200 trillion cubic feet. Terry and Winger consider this a "reasonable minimum estimate based upon present evidence." [8]

Two other estimates, not included in Table 9, concern the offshore gas reserves only. Kastrop, in discussing the Gulf Coast offshore province, mentions that "some have estimated as much as . . . 70 trillion cubic feet of natural gas are to be found ultimately" in this area alone.[9] The U. S. Geological Survey has estimated total continental shelf natural gas resources as 68.5 trillion cubic feet, slightly lower than Kastrop's reference.[10]

## Reserve Estimates and the Resource Base

Each of the estimates of total future natural gas supply discussed in the previous section has as a common basis a double assumption—(a) an estimate of total future crude oil supply (derived from an estimate of ultimate reserves), and (b) a gas-oil ratio applied to the crude oil figure. This compounding of assumptions naturally leads to considerable variation in results. Different crude oil assumptions are used, and the gas-oil ratios employed vary from Hubbert's 7,500 to the Department of the Interior's 3,333.[11] At this point it is possible to say that in the present context some of the figures

[8] L. F. Terry and J. G. Winger, "Sees 1,200 Trillion cf U. S. Recoverable Gas," *American Gas Association Monthly,* xxxix, Nos. 7-8 (July-August, 1957), 39.

[9] J. E. Kastrop, "Louisiana's Offshore Picture," *The Petroleum Engineer,* xxvii, No. 13 (December, 1955), B-40.

[10] American Petroleum Institute, *Petroleum Facts and Figures* (11th ed.; 1954), p. 120.

[11] The Interior Department gas-oil ratio is deduced from their estimate of ultimate oil reserves at 300 billion barrels (see p. 19) and the use of the estimate of one quadrillion cubic feet as "ultimate gas reserves."

appear to be unduly conservative because of the low oil-reserve figure on which they are based. Terry's first estimate is now obsolete; the Pogue and Hill, and Hubbert estimates are associated with oil estimates in the low group (see p. 19). Nevertheless it is instructive to consider the estimates in the larger perspective of the resource base, as was done earlier in the discussion of oil.

With the exception of the Interior Department estimate, the proved-reserve basis of the total future supply estimates means that they all contain the current technology limitation; the estimates refer only to gas that is (or would be) recoverable with techniques and under economic conditions prevailing here and now. There is a paucity of information on the recovery factor in gas production, but the Bureau of Statistics of the American Gas Association has furnished an estimate that the "ratio of proved economically recoverable natural gas to total original gas in place within a given reservoir averages approximately 75 to 80 per cent." [12] This estimate is taken here as representative of authoritative, technical opinion.

It will be recalled that the conversion of the ultimate oil reserve estimates to the resource-base equivalent was accomplished by multiplying the ultimate-reserve estimate by the reciprocal of the recovery factor. The procedure cannot be so neat or simple with the gas estimates. The total future supply estimates contain current proved reserves, whereas the recovery factor as given relates to original reserves. The recovery factor cannot be applied to current proved reserves because the production of gas from a reservoir changes the percentage recovery that will be obtained from the remaining gas. Without attempting to compute the original reserves of known reservoirs with current proved reserves, the best that can be done is to calculate a "minimum approximation" of the resource-base equivalent of the future supply estimates. The figures in column 3 of Table 9 represent the "proved reserves" (in the sense of total cumulative production to be

[12] Personal communication.

expected in the future) of the reservoirs as yet undiscovered, and hence can appropriately be multiplied by the reciprocal of the recovery factor. Current proved reserves cannot be so expanded but it is known they do not include the total gas in place in known reservoirs. Thus the result of this multiplication, shown in Table 10 as the minimum resource-base equivalent of the total future supply estimates, understates this equivalent by an unknown amount.

Column 2 of Table 10 lists the total future supply estimates as given in column 2 of Table 9. The figures in column 3 result from division of the undiscovered portion of the estimates (listed in column 3 of Table 9) by 0.8—the upper range of estimated current recovery, chosen to give current technology the benefit of the doubt and to make the minimum resource base equivalent somewhat more conservative—and from addition of proved reserves as of the time of the estimate. Column 4 provides a measure of the relative magnitude of the minimum resource-base equivalents in terms of current production levels.

TABLE 10

*Estimates of Total Future Natural Gas Supply Converted to Minimum Resource-Base Equivalent*

(In trillion cubic feet)

| Estimate and date (1) | Total future supply (2) | Minimum resource-base equivalent (3) | Ratio of col. 3 to 1956 production (4) |
|---|---|---|---|
| Terry, 1950 (a) | 510 | 592 | 54 |
| Hinson, 1954 (b) | 586 | 681 | 62 |
| Interior Dept., 1956 (c) | 875 | 1,041 | 95 |
| Pratt, 1956 (d) | 725 | 853 | 78 |
| Pogue & Hill, 1956 (e) | 570 | 660 | 60 |
| Hubbert, 1956 (f) | 735 | 863 | 78 |
| Terry & Winger, 1957 (g) | 1,200 | 1,230 | 113 |

SOURCES: See Table 9.

The gas-oil ratio, the second basis of the several estimates, has yet to be examined, but before doing so it will be helpful to consider the estimates of future gas production. The determinants of future domestic natural gas supply can then be viewed as they relate to both the reserve-resource and production estimates.

## ESTIMATES OF FUTURE PRODUCTION

### Description of Estimates

The earlier discussion (see p. 25), concerning the implied demand level in future oil production estimates and the relevance of those estimates to the availability approach used herein, also applies to estimates for natural gas. The various gas estimates are summarized in Table 11: the estimates themselves are listed in column 4; column 2 denotes whether the production for the year shown in column 3 is projected as the historical peak by the author of the estimate; column 6 shows the estimates as percentages of the 1956 production (10.9 trillion cubic feet).

The figure attributed to the President's Materials Policy Commission is taken from a table in Vol. I of the Commission's report which portrays "A Hypothetical Picture of Energy Flow in 1975." Although there are discussions of future possibilities at several places in the five volumes of the report, the only specific comment on the subject is the acceptance of "relatively optimistic assumptions . . . as to future discovery." [13]

[13] *Resources for Freedom,* Report of the President's Materials Policy Commission (Washington, D. C.: U. S. Government Printing Office, 1952), I, 127.

TABLE 11

## Estimates of Future U.S. Natural Gas Production

| Source and date (1) | Peak (2) | Year (3) | Production (trillion cubic feet) (4) | Explicit total future supply(*) or implied minimum future supply through terminal date as of January 1, 1957 (trillion cubic feet) (5) | Per cent of 1956 production (6) |
|---|---|---|---|---|---|
| PMPC, 1951 (a) | | 1975 | 15.3 | 555 minimum | 140 |
| Egloff, 1951 (b) | | 1960 | 11.4 | } 680 minimum | 105 |
| | | 1975 | 18.0 | | 165 |
| Pettyjohn, 1955 (c) | X | 1960 | 12.0 | 288 minimum | 110 |
| Ayres, 1955 (d) | X | 1965 | 12.0 | } *600 | 110 |
| | | 1975 | 11.0 | | 101 |
| Interior Dept., 1956 (e) | | 1975 | 19.0 | *875 | 174 |
| Pratt, 1956 (f) | | 1965 | 13.5 | } *725 | 124 |
| | | 1975 | 15.0 | | 138 |
| Pogue & Hill, 1956 (g) | | 1965 | 14.2 | 392 minimum | 130 |
| | | 1965 | 15.2 | ⎤ | 139 |
| | X | 1970 | 16.0 | } *570 | 147 |
| | | 1975 | 15.5 | ⎦ | 142 |
| A.G.A., 1956 (h) | | 1975 | 22.5 | *850 | 206 |
| Tippy, 1956 (i) | X | 1970 | 13.0 | } *475 | 119 |
| | | 1975 | 12.5 | | 115 |
| | X | 1975 | 15.0 | *725 | 138 |
| | X | 1980 | 17.0 | *875 | 156 |
| Hubbert, 1956 (j) | X | 1970 | 14.0 | } *725 | 128 |
| | | 1975 | 13.5 | | 124 |
| Ayres, 1956 (k) | X | 1965-70 | 13.0 | *600 | 119 |
| Terry & Winger, 1957 (l) | | 1966 | 16.3 | } *1,200 | 150 |
| | X | 1980-90 | 20.0 | | 183 |

[For sources see p. 76.]

Egloff also does not present specific support of his estimate, but in a subsequent article on the subject he cites Terry's original reserve estimate, commenting that it is a very conservative figure. Essentially his position is the same as the one he takes regarding the future of oil—only a very small fraction of the possible occurrence has been probed. His outlook is summed up in the statement that "estimators" (whom he does not name) "consider that supplies will be maintained well beyond the present century." [14]

Pettyjohn merely mentions in passing that "it has been estimated" that a peak production of 12 trillion cubic feet of gas will occur in 1960.[15] Ayres derives his estimates

[14] G. Egloff, "The Place of Natural Gas, Present and Future," *Proceedings,* American Gas Association, 1952, p. 32.

[15] E. S. Pettyjohn, "Coal . . . Gas Source of the Future," *Coal Age,* LX, No. 3 (March, 1955), p. 57.

---

SOURCES, TABLE 11:

(a) *Resources for Freedom,* President's Materials Policy Commission (Washington, D. C.: U. S. Government Printing Office, 1952), I, 127 f.

(b) *Ibid.,* IV, 193.

(c) E. S. Pettyjohn, "Coal . . . Gas Source of the Future," *Coal Age,* LX, No. 3 (March, 1955), 57.

(d) E. Ayres, "Energy Resources for the Future," *Oil and Gas Compact Bulletin,* XIV, No. 1 (June, 1955), 21.

(e) Joint Committee on Atomic Energy, *Peaceful Uses of Atomic Energy,* Report of the Panel on the Impact of the Peaceful Uses of Atomic Energy (Washington, D. C.: U. S. Government Printing Office, January, 1956), II, 87.

(f) *Ibid.,* II, 92.

(g) J. E. Pogue and K. E. Hill, *Future Growth and Financial Requirements of the World Petroleum Industry* (New York: Chase Manhattan Bank, 1956). Presented at annual meeting of the American Institute of Mining, Metallurgical and Petroleum Engineers, Petroleum Branch, February 21, 1956.

(h) Bureau of Statistics, American Gas Association, "Supply of, and Demand for, Natural Gas in 1975," August 3, 1956.

(i) W. B. Tippy, "Where Does the Gas Industry Go from Here?" *American Gas Journal,* XVIII, No. 3 (October, 1956), 66-67.

(j) M. K. Hubbert, "Nuclear Energy and the Fossil Fuels," *Drilling and Production Practice—1956* (New York: American Petroleum Institute, 1957), p. 18.

(k) E. Ayres, "The Fuel Situation," *Scientific American,* 195, No. 4 (October, 1956), 47.

(l) L. F. Terry and J. G. Winger, "Sees 1,200 Trillion of U. S. Recoverable Gas," *American Gas Association Monthly,* XXXIX, Nos. 7-8 (July-August, 1957), 10 ff.

through the same decline-curve technique he used for his oil estimates (see p. 29). He obtains his figures from a total future supply of 600 trillion cubic feet, which he assumes arbitrarily as a recognition of Terry's characterization of his own total supply estimate as too conservative.[16]

The Interior Department estimate is in the form of a statement that a 1975 demand of 19 trillion cubic feet can be met "if exploratory drilling for petroleum and gas continue to increase over the next 25 years, as seems inevitable." [17] Pratt's figures are presented as the estimated consumption in 1965 and 1975, but since he makes no mention of imports it is assumed here that his figures are equivalent to production estimates.

The several Pogue and Hill figures appearing in Table 11 have a double basis. The estimate of 14.2 trillion cubic feet for 1965 production is based on "discovery momentum," that is, an assumption that future annual discoveries will average 25 per cent more than those of the postwar period to date at the same time that the proved reserve-production ratio falls from 22 to 20 during the period 1956–65. The other three estimates of Pogue and Hill are derived from a decline curve based on the assumption of 570 trillion cubic feet of total future supply. The figures for 1970 and 1975 are interpolated from Figure 11 of the Pogue and Hill paper.

The basis of the American Gas Association estimate is summarized in their statement as follows:

The reasoning in this memorandum assumes that appropriate economic incentives will be present to foster an accelerated discovery rate so that new supplies will become available when needed for supplying the nation's increased demands. It also assumes that deliverability will be maintained adequately to provide the increased requirements of natural gas in spite of declining pressures in some of the older producing fields. Presumable technological improvements in recovery technique will assist in this area by per-

[16] Terry expressed this opinion publicly prior to the presentation of his 1957 paper in which he more than doubled his original estimate (see p. 70).
[17] Joint Committee on Atomic Energy, *op. cit.*, II, 87.

mitting substantially higher proportions of gas in underground reservoirs to be made economically available.[18]

In addition, the estimate is based on a figure of 850 trillion cubic feet total future supply.

Tippy's several estimates are taken from decline curves based on varying total future supply assumptions. (The estimate for the non-peak year 1975 is read from Chart 4 of Tippy's paper.) Hubbert notes that the 14 trillion-cubic-foot peak is "about the maximum that appears likely while allowing for the necessary period of prolonged decline," and comments that Pratt's 1975 estimate requires a total future supply "considerably in excess" of Pratt's total reserve assumption.

Ayres' most recent estimate is a revision of his previous figure, again using the decline-curve method. He projects his curve on the "conservative assumption" that gas production will increase at about 4 per cent per year, about half the present rate, during the next few years. Ayres contends that the peak will be held down by the fact that as the peak is approached, pipeline builders "will hesitate to build new lines if they are not assured that the gas will last long enough to amortize their investment." [19]

The Terry and Winger estimate for 1966 assumes an annual growth rate in demand of 4.7 per cent in the coming decade. Their peak estimate of 20 trillion cubic feet in the 1980–90 decade is indicated by a rough decline curve which they fit to their total future supply estimate. Although a figure for 1975 could be taken from this curve, it would place more emphasis on the curve than the authors themselves are willing to do, since they imply that it is only one of the many possible curves that can be based on their total future supply estimate. Noting that the latter "is taken as a conservative minimum," they conclude, "we expect that future reviewers

[18] Bureau of Statistics, American Gas Association, "Supply of, and Demand for, Natural Gas in 1975," August 3, 1956, p. 6.

[19] E. Ayres, "The Fuel Situation," *Scientific American*, 195, No. 4 (October, 1956), 46.

will probably find the curve too small and the indicated peak to occur later than here forecast."[20]

Column 5 of Table 11 compares the production estimates on the basis of the implied or explicitly stated reserve magnitude to which they are related. The figures marked with asterisks are the total future supply assumptions from which the production estimates were derived or to which they are related. Some of these assumptions are not listed in Table 9 and considered individually because they are only hypothetical total supply levels, viz. "If we assume a total future supply of 10, then production in year T should be Z." The unmarked figures in column 5 were computed in a similar manner to the equivalent figures in Table 4. Specifically, (a) a straight-line growth in production was assumed from 1956 to the terminal year or between intermediate years, if noted; (b) an allowance of a proved-reserve-production ratio of 20 was made for the terminal year. This ratio was chosen because of its common use as the proved-reserve basis in the supply contracts for transmission pipelines. Again, the straight-line growth and reserve-production ratio are arbitrary assumptions adopted solely to provide a basis for comparing the *minimum* total future supply implied by the various production estimates.

### Comparison of Estimates

Table 11 can be summarized as follows: (a) estimates of the *year of peak production* (columns 2 and 3) range from 1960 past 1980, (b) estimates of *peak output* (columns 2 and 4), where specified in the period through 1975, range from 12 trillion to 16 trillion cubic feet, (c) estimates of *output in 1975* (column 4) range from 11.0 to 22.5 trillion cubic feet. As would be expected from the wide variation in the bases of the estimates, there is also a wide range among the estimates themselves. And, also in accordance with expectation, the

[20] Terry and Winger, *op. cit.*

estimates of 1975 output show a rough correlation with the total future supply estimate with which they are associated:

| Range of explicit total future supply estimates listed in Table 11 | Number of corresponding 1975 output estimates in Table 11 | Average of corresponding 1975 output estimates in Table 11 |
|---|---|---|
| 475 | 1 | 12.5 |
| 570-600 | 2 | 13.25 |
| 725 | 3 | 14.5 |
| 850-875 | 2 | 20.7 |

The favored basis of estimation is the decline curve. The conceptual limitation of this technique has been discussed above with respect to the oil estimates, and here the estimates demonstrate in addition the dependence of the results on the judgments of the estimator, despite the fact that the estimate is mathematically derived. Five of the authors listed in Table 11 use the technique to obtain an estimate for 1975 production. Ayres, with a total future supply assumption of 600 trillion cubic feet, gets a 1975 output of 11 trillion. Yet Tippy, using 475 trillion cubic feet [21] and Pogue and Hill, with 570 trillion cubic feet, get results of 12.5 trillion and 15.5 trillion respectively, as 1975 output—a total future supply estimate smaller than Ayres' yields a higher projected output for the same year. Again, Tippy and Hubbert, using the same total future supply assumption of 725 trillion cubic feet, project 1975 output as 15 trillion and 13.5 trillion, respectively, a difference of 11 per cent when using the same basis.

Nevertheless, it is not intended to deny that there is any relationship between the reserve-resource position and the level of future production in a given year. Obviously there is at any time a level of output beyond which production would

[21] Tippy uses an adjusted Terry figure of 600 trillion cubic feet for total future supply as if it were an ultimate-reserve estimate. It has been converted here to a total future supply equivalent.

be uneconomic, if not physically impossible, because of the reserve-resource position. But one of the principal arguments of this study is that there should be room for the exercise of judgment with regard to *all* the determinants of future output levels, not the reserve-resource aspect alone, in estimating future output.

## TECHNOLOGY AS A DETERMINANT OF FUTURE DOMESTIC NATURAL GAS AVAILABILITY

### Discovery

The fundamental fact concerning natural gas discovery is that much of it is intimately and inextricably related to the search for oil. Until the post-war era and the creation of a nation-wide market for gas, the discovery of new reservoirs could be described as the result of a search for oil, not gas. The post-war rise in the value of gas has stimulated the search for gas in known gas areas, but as long as oil is the more valuable commodity, it is reasonable to assume that a large portion of gas discoveries will continue to be a by-product of oil discovery efforts.

Appropriately, then, the general conclusions with respect to oil discovery prospects which were reached in the preceding section apply equally to natural gas. It will be recalled that these conclusions are optimistic because there are large unexplored areas, among which the continental shelf is prominent; there are further possibilities in known productive areas; there are unexplored possibilities everywhere at greater depth; there are undetermined potentials in unorthodox sources; and there is room for further exploitation of current discovery technology. For all of these reasons the general outlook for gas discovery (considering associated and non-associated together) is also considered good.

At the same time it is necessary to note a peculiarity of current proved gas reserves—a large percentage of total proved reserves are in a few giant, non-associated gas fields, which "accumulated" over the preceding forty years because there was no market, or at best a limited market, for the gas. In Texas, which contains almost one-half the total proved reserves of natural gas in the United States, some three-quarters of the total state reserves are non-associated reserves, and are largely contained in twenty-two major fields.[22] (The total number of gas fields in Texas in 1956 was 1,755.) [23]

Moreover, the giant fields are a proportionately larger source of current supply than the smaller fields, since they constitute the logical first source to tap with long-distance transmission pipelines. Thus the great expansion in natural gas production in the past decade has been disproportionately from the giant fields. Although associated and non-associated discoveries will continue in the future, it appears questionable whether the number of giant non-associated fields discovered will be sufficient to maintain the present ratio between associated reserves on the one hand and non-associated reserves on the other. As shown in Table 12, a small but evident decline in the proportion of non-associated reserves has been taking place since World War II. It is reasonable to expect this trend to continue, and it may perhaps even accelerate.

The crucial element in estimating the total future natural gas supply remains the choice of the appropriate gas-oil ratio. There is a limitation in this choice, arising from the fact that none of the ratios derivable from published statistics can be a measure of the *true* ratio between the natural occurrence of oil and natural gas, since none of the data refers to the actual reservoir content of total gas and oil in place. Both production and proved reserves depend on the recovery factor. The problem, then, is to determine whether

---

[22] C. A. Breitung, "Present Available Natural Gas Reserves in Texas as of January 1, 1956," *Proceedings,* Ninth Oil Recovery Conference, Bulletin No. 54, Texas Petroleum Research Committee, April 9-10, 1956, pp. 10-26.
[23] *Ibid.,* p. 12.

TABLE 12

## Non-associated Reserves as a Percentage of Total Proved Reserves of Natural Gas*

| Year | Percentage |
|------|------------|
| 1956 | 67.3 |
| 1955 | 68.4 |
| 1954 | 69.4 |
| 1953 | 69.8 |
| 1952 | 69.1 |
| 1951 | 69.2 |
| 1950 | 70.5 |
| 1949 | 70.0 |
| 1948 | 71.0 |
| 1947 | 72.2 |
| 1946 | 72.5 |

* Excluding reserves in underground storage.

despite this limitation there is a useful measure among the several ratio choices available from published data.

One possible choice is the ratio of the proved reserves of associated gas to the proved reserves of oil. This indicates the relative abundance of recoverable oil and gas where they occur together in the same reservoir. Table 13 lists this ratio for recent years.

Table 13 seems to indicate a slight rise in this gas to oil ratio over time. The average of the last six years is 5.5 per cent greater than that of the first six years, and figures for 1955 and 1956 are considerably higher than for anything in previous years. But the figures are ambiguous—they may mean that recently discovered reservoirs have a higher gas-oil ratio than older ones, or they may merely reflect the different courses of gas and oil production, which are among the determinants of the proved-reserve position. About all that

TABLE 13

### Ratio of Associated Gas to Oil in Proved Reserves

| Year | cf/bbl |
|------|--------|
| 1956 | 2,505 |
| 1955 | 2,342 |
| 1954 | 2,177 |
| 1953 | 2,225 |
| 1952 | 2,196 |
| 1951 | 2,169 |
| 1950 | 2,162 |
| 1949 | 2,190 |
| 1948 | 2,116 |
| 1947 | 2,149 |
| 1946 | 2,114 |
| Average | 2,213 |

can be concluded is that the ratio of oil and gas in proved reserves, where they occur in conjunction, has been between 2,000 and 3,000 cubic feet per barrel of oil and that it may be rising.

Another possible measure of the oil-gas relationship is the ratio in the cumulative production of both gas and oil. Through 1956 this ratio was 4.0 Mcf per barrel of oil, based on Bureau of Mines statistics. (The ratio in 1956 production was 4,275 cubic feet per barrel.) But the record of "production" has included wastage only since 1935, so that the ratio on this basis cannot be said to bear much relationship to the ratio of recoverable oil to *recoverable* gas. In addition, the production of oil and of non-associated gas have no relationship whatever.

A third possibility is the ratio in cumulative discoveries

(production plus wastage plus present proved reserves) of both gas and oil. In his original work on total future supply of natural gas, Terry attempted to estimate the wastage to obtain such a ratio. He estimated that about 30 trillion cubic feet had been lost and wasted in the natural gas industry through 1949, and "an enormous but unknown quantity of gas in solution with oil . . . wasted in the production of oil," so that total gas "produced" through 1949, including marketed production, was from 150 to 175 trillion cubic feet.[24] Terry thus estimated the additional wastage of gas in oil production at 36 to 61 trillion cubic feet. He rounded his cumulative "production" figure to 160 trillion cubic feet, implying 46 trillion cubic feet of such wastage, for a total loss of 76 trillion cubic feet including wastage in the natural gas industry. When Terry's cumulative totals are carried through 1956, the resultant gas-oil ratio is 5.4 Mcf/bbl. (Terry obtained a ratio of 4.1. The reason for the increase is the much higher ratio in recent discoveries than in the past. See discussion below.)

The usefulness of this ratio depends upon two things: the accuracy of the wastage estimate and the degree to which discoveries are a reflection of the ratio of *occurrence* of recoverable oil to recoverable gas rather than mere discovery experience. In view of the large quantities of gas wastage involved, the large range of the wastage estimate and the lack of any detailed basis for the estimate, Terry's figure is of little use here. The discovery aspect is considered separately below.

A fourth possibility is the ratio in current proved reserves, which was 7.8 Mcf/bbl as of 1956. Here again past wastage is an element of error. The gas that was wasted in the past, if it had not been wasted, would be in the ground today, and would be part of proved reserves. In the strict sense this is not true; that is, the very same gas that was wasted might not be part of proved reserves today, since it might have been

[24] L. F. Terry, "The Future Supply of Natural Gas," *Proceedings*, American Gas Association, 1950, p. 157.

produced in place of other gas that entered into production, because of more favorable location or mere chance. But *net* production would have remained unchanged if there had never been any waste, for the only limitation on production was demand, not supply. Thus proved reserves of gas, as a net or residual quantity, would have been larger throughout the history of the oil and gas industry. Since no suitable estimate of wastage exists, the proved-reserve ratio understates the true situation to an unknown degree.

A more serious drawback, however, is the fact that proved reserves, as a net or residual quantity, are as much a function of production as of discovery, being the net result of both activities. Proved reserves of oil have tended to bear a rather constant relationship to production, but for several decades prior to the era since World War II gas reserves tended to mount because of the lack of a market for what was found. Gas reserves therefore reflect the course of previous production as much as the fruits of discovery, and introduce an indeterminate error in the other direction.

This leads to consideration of the fifth possibility, the discovery ratio. To the extent that discovery activity is chiefly a search for oil the results of that activity, through the unexpected findings of gas, would reflect the natural ratio of occurrence between recoverable oil and recoverable gas. On the other hand, to the extent that discovery effort is deliberately for gas alone and is independent of the oil search, the ratio reflects the value of gas (i.e., a higher value of gas stimulates the search for gas, hence leads to greater gas discoveries relative to oil discoveries). To complicate the matter, the definition of proved reserves leads to two kinds of discoveries as defined in the statistics: "Extensions and revisions" which are the result of the development of known fields, and which are "discoveries" only in the sense that they are additions to proved reserves through the proof of what was previously suspected or expected; and, secondly, "Discoveries of new fields and new pools in old fields" which are the result of exploration in the true sense, known as "wildcatting." This exploration is undertaken with, at the most, indirect evidence of the possible occurrence of oil or gas, and sometimes in the absence of any evidence at all.

Which of these discovery ratios is most representative of the relative abundance, in the ground, of recoverable oil and recoverable gas? The ratio in "old" pools and fields, as revealed in the figures for extensions and revisions, is invalid to the extent that it depends on the specific characteristics of the pools and fields being developed. Those in which development is essentially completed (hence contribute little to the "discovery" statistics) are not adequately represented in the ratio. The ratio in new pools and fields alone is a truer representation of discovery, yet there is an advantage to a third ratio—in total "discoveries" or additions to proved reserves—in the sense that they constitute a larger sample.

The significance of the choice between the three discovery ratios is demonstrated in Table 14. During the period for

TABLE 14

## Gas-Oil Ratio in Discoveries of Proved Reserves

(Cubic feet per barrel)

| Year | Extensions and revisions | New fields and pools | Total discoveries |
|------|--------------------------|----------------------|-------------------|
| 1956 | 7,664 | 11,850 | 8,355 |
| 1955 | 6,812 | 11,991 | 7,666 |
| 1954 | 2,025 | 8,479 | 3,462 |
| 1953 | 4,944 | 11,969 | 6,205 |
| 1952 | 3,966 | 10,900 | 5,218 |
| 1951 | 3,233 | 7,808 | 3,637 |
| 1950 | 4,591 | 5,093 | 4,702 |
| 1949 | 3,509 | 5,180 | 3,976 |
| 1948 | 2,874 | 10,414 | 3,662 |
| 1947 | 3,749 | 7,656 | 4,455 |
| Average | 4,437 | 9,134 | 5,134 |

SOURCE: Annual proved-reserve estimates of American Petroleum Institute and American Gas Association.

which proved-reserve statistics are available the gas-oil ratio in new fields and new pools has been consistently higher than that in extensions and revisions, averaging more than double during the ten-year period. (The ratio in total discoveries is closer to that in extensions and revisions because of the great preponderance of the latter in the total.) Thus the use of a ratio based on one or the other can yield widely varying estimates of total future supply. The immediate question, however, is not what the choice should be, but why there is a dramatic difference between the results of wildcatting and of the development of known pools and fields.

One factor would appear to be depth and its relation to the gas-oil ratio. Terry describes this as follows: "Since gas is compressed somewhat in proportion to pressure, the quantity, by weight, of gas contained in a cubic foot of pore space is greater with increasing depth . . . Deposits of oil found at great depths and under correspondingly high pressure contain larger proportions of gas in solution than oil in shallow reservoirs." Moreover, at greater depths the proportion of free gas present is likely to be greater, "since the deeper the deposit the higher the reservoir temperature and the greater the possibility for more complete transformation of the original oil in place with resulting increased formation of gas." [25]

Statistics on the distribution of existing wells by depth are lacking, and for new wells the statistics are available for only a few years, but it is known that a very high proportion of all development wells are in shallow pools less than 4,000 feet below the surface. (See Table 7.) The proportion of deep wildcats, on the other hand (those 10,000 feet and below), has been increasing (see Table 6), and discoveries at these depths come to constitute a correspondingly higher proportion of total wildcat discoveries. Further, the wildcatting in

[25] *Ibid.*, p. 158.
Weeks (personal communication) suggests in addition the possibility that gas may flush oil from the deeper reservoirs, causing it to migrate up-dip into shallower traps.

the offshore Gulf province is deep drilling, and both the success ratio and gas-oil ratio are high.[26]

On the other hand, it is possible that the difference between the gas-oil ratio in wildcatting and in development has a non-geologic basis. The ratio may reflect the rapid increase in the field price of natural gas in the post-war era which, through anticipation of still higher prices, would lead to more wildcatting for gas and a consequent higher ratio. Thus Table 15 shows that in this period the proportion of additions to reserves from wildcatting to total additions to reserves in gas has consistently been higher than the same proportion in oil, and the ratio between the two proportions

TABLE 15

*Yearly Additions to Reserves in New Fields and Pools as Percentage of Total Yearly Additions to Reserves*

| Year | In oil | In gas | Ratio, oil to gas |
|---|---|---|---|
| 1956 | 15.7% | 22.7% | 1.44 |
| 1955 | 16.6 | 26.0 | 1.56 |
| 1954 | 20.4 | 51.7 | 2.53 |
| 1953 | 18.0 | 34.6 | 1.92 |
| 1952 | 18.0 | 37.7 | 2.09 |
| 1951 | 8.8 | 18.9 | 2.14 |
| 1950 | 22.0 | 23.9 | 1.08 |
| 1949 | 27.9 | 36.4 | 1.30 |
| 1948 | 10.4 | 29.7 | 2.85 |
| 1947 | 18.1 | 31.0 | 1.71 |
| Average | | | 1.86 |

[26] *Petroleum Week*, IV, No. 8 (February 22, 1957), 41-70; also I. H. Cram, "The Outlook Offshore," paper given at meeting of American Petroleum Institute, Chicago, November 14, 1956.

Gulf Coast offshore wells currently *average* 9,700 feet in depth; by 1970 such wells are expected to *average* over 12,000 feet. (See C. R. Graham, "The Big Offshore Picture—to 1970," *The Petroleum Engineer*, XXIX, No. 5 [May, 1957], B-21—B-27). Wildcats will lead the way down, and can be expected to be consistently deeper, on the average, than the average for all wells.

has averaged 1.86 in the past ten years. (That is, the proportion of wildcat discoveries to total discoveries of gas in each
year has averaged 1.86 times the same proportion in oil for
that year.) To the extent that this influence holds, the gas-
oil ratio in wildcat discoveries is a reflection of the relative
value of gas.

For present purposes, it is not necessary to decide which
of the two influences, depth or value, is primarily or wholly
responsible for the higher gas-oil ratio in wildcat discoveries.
It can be assumed that future discoveries will be deeper on
the average and that the value of natural gas will certainly
not fall, and may even continue its present rising trend (see
below). On balance, therefore, it seems reasonable to use a
figure higher than Terry's but not on the order of recent
wildcat experience. A ratio of 7,000 is chosen here as a figure
higher than 6,000 that is not too drastic an increase. Ad-
mittedly, as an arbitrary choice this is no more refined than
the ratio assumptions used in preceding estimates of total
future natural gas supply, but at least it reflects the position
developed here that the ratios previously used are too low.


## Production Aspects

Again, the general conclusions regarding drilling technology and the exploitation of the offshore provinces that
were reached in the discussion of oil apply equally well to
natural gas. There are in addition certain physical limitations on gas production that require mention.

Since dissolved gas (known as "casinghead" gas to producers) is produced by oil wells, it is difficult or even impossible to vary the rate of production independently of the oil
production of the well. Its availability is thus determined by
the rate of oil production. To some extent this is modified
by state conservation regulations, as in Texas, where the
common permissible gas-oil ratio in oil well output is 2,000
cubic feet per barrel. That is, the production of casinghead

gas from a given oil well normally cannot exceed this ratio; any excess gas "produced" by the well must be recycled back to the reservoir.

The prime reason for such control is to conserve reservoir energy and thus increase the total primary production of oil from the reservoir. This same objective applied to a gas cap tends to postpone gas production until the primary-oil-producing life of the reservoir is about exhausted. The degree to which this may be necessary or desirable depends on many factors—for example, the gas-oil ratio in a reservoir. With a minor quantity of oil present, the reservoir may be treated as a non-associated gas occurrence. The significant distinction, however, is that the output of gas wells from a gas cap occurrence is not closely related to the rate of oil output from the reservoir.

The recovery factor for gas has been mentioned above. One of the recovery limitations is imposed by the presumed sealing off of small pockets of gas in the reservoir through the encroachment of water as gas is withdrawn and the pressure declines. The formation of such small pockets may not be detectable or, if known, their recovery may not be worth the necessary special measures. In addition to such "secondary resources" there are also those noted above (see p. 66), which are known to exist but which on economic criteria have been excluded from the estimate of proved reserves. A third category of such resources is the gas content of a reservoir below its abandonment pressure, hence also excluded from the reserve estimate. Finally, there is the dissolved gas content of secondary oil resources; such gas probably cannot be recovered except through production of the oil, so if the oil is secondary, the gas is also.

It would be advantageous to have some idea of the extent of known "secondary reserves" of gas, such as were provided by Torrey for oil. Since they cannot be quantified the most that can be said is that there exists an unknown quantity of gas which will become available given improved gas recovery techniques (such as "fracturing" to increase the effective permeability of the area around a gas well, thus making it economically feasible to carry a given reservoir to a lower abandonment pressure) and as secondary oil resources are utilized.

## CONCLUSIONS ON DOMESTIC NATURAL

## GAS AVAILABILITY

The first step in deriving conclusions on domestic natural gas availability in 1975 is to estimate total future supply. Due to the absence of data there is no alternative to the method used by all previous estimators—the application of an assumed gas-oil ratio to an assumed future oil supply.

The ratio adopted above is 7,000 cubic feet per barrel, and the resource base for future oil production has been estimated to be on the order of 500 billion barrels. The gas-oil ratio is, however, in terms of current recoverability, since it is derived from data based on the proved reserve concept. Thus the figure of 500 must be converted back to a current recoverability basis by dividing by three (the reverse of the resource base conversion), which yields a figure of 167 billion barrels. When the above gas-oil ratio is applied to this, the result is 1.169 quadrillion cubic feet of gas; and if this in turn is converted to a resource-base equivalent by dividing by a factor of 0.8 there is an indicated quantity of almost 1.5 quadrillion cubic feet potentially available for future recovery. The latter can be passed over in this instance since, due to the relatively high level of recovery that already exists, the total supply available for future production should be on the order indicated whether no improvement in recovery levels occurs or whether full recovery is attained. The difference between the two figures, in other words, is within the error of estimation.

It will be seen that the total future supply estimate derived here is, in round numbers, the same as that of Terry
and Winger, although the basis is different. Nevertheless,
this study in effect agrees with those authors that the total
future supply of natural gas in the light of present knowledge
is on the order of 1.2 quadrillion cubic feet.

There remains to be considered the availability of natural
gas in the year 1975. As a first step, existing estimates of natural gas output in that year are referred to. None of the estimates for that year in Table 11 is related to a total future
supply estimate as large as that adopted here (although, as
noted above, the Terry and Winger estimate for 1980 is the
same figure adopted here). The highest existing estimate
for 1975 is related to a total future supply estimate of 850
trillion cubic feet. In adopting an estimate of 1975 availability for present purposes it is instructive to test this highest estimate—the A.G.A. figure of 22.5 trillion cubic feet—
for plausibility.

What does the A.G.A. figure imply in relation to the oil
availability estimate developed above? It was concluded that
domestic primary availability in 1975 would be some 4.0
billion barrels, and secondary availability would be on the
order of 2.0 billion barrels. But secondary output must be
ignored on the presumption that, being secondary, the reservoir energy is essentially exhausted, hence the gas available
from secondary output would be negligible. On this basis a
gas output of 22.5 trillion cubic feet would mean a gas-oil
ratio of 5,625 cubic feet per barrel of primary oil output.
Although this is 32 per cent greater than the 1956 production
ratio of 4,275, it is consistent with the conclusions previously
stated concerning a higher gas-oil ratio in the future than in
the past.

A second ratio implied in the A.G.A. estimate relative to
the above oil availability estimate is that of associated gas
output to oil output. Assuming a ratio of 2,500 cubic feet
per barrel, the highest level yet recorded in proved reserves

(see Table 13),[27] the output of associated gas in 1975 would be 48 per cent of total gas output. Dissolved gas alone currently accounts for 33 per cent of total current output (see Table 16, column "f"), so that total associated gas constitutes a greater but unknown proportion of the total.

It is apparent from the foregoing that a level of gas output such as estimated by the A.G.A. carries with it in the present study certain key assumptions:

1. A high gas-oil ratio in total output, and
2. Either (a) a high gas-oil ratio where the hydrocarbons occur together, or (b) a very high gas-oil ratio in future discoveries, sufficient to allow future non-associated gas discoveries to replace the proved reserves in giant gas fields which currently constitute a large proportion of total proved reserves.

Assumptions (1) and (2-a) are consistent with the general conclusions reached previously in this study, but it is also clear that any higher figure for 1975 gas output would begin to stretch this consistency. It was concluded above that the proportion of non-associated gas in total proved reserves is likely to decline. To the extent that this occurs, more of the yearly output must come from associated reserves. But this, in turn, means that gas output is to a greater extent a function of oil output, and the higher the estimated gas output, the higher the required ratio for associated gas. Thus the A.G.A. figure of 22.5 trillion cubic feet must be taken, on the basis of present knowledge, as the limit of domestic natural gas availability in 1975 despite the fact that this study obtains a higher total future supply estimate than that to which the A.G.A. figure for 1975 is related.

[27] Unfortunately, there are no production statistics for associated gas alone. Figures are available for gas from oil wells and gas from gas wells (see Table 16). The former gives dissolved gas output, but the latter includes both gas from gas caps and gas from non-associated gas reservoirs.

## Gas Withdrawal and Disposition, 1935–1956

(In billion cubic feet)

| Year | Total gross withdrawal (a) | From gas wells (b) | From oil wells (c) | Marketed production (d) | Repressuring (e) | Oil per cent of total $\frac{c}{a}$ (f) | Marketed per cent of total $\frac{d}{a}$ (g) | Repressuring per cent of total $\frac{e}{a}$ (h) |
|---|---|---|---|---|---|---|---|---|
| 1956 | 12,373 | 8,307 | 4,066 | 10,082 | 1,427 | 32.9 | 81.5 | 11.5 |
| 1955 | 11,720 | 7,842 | 3,878 | 9,405 | 1,541 | 33.1 | 80.2 | 13.1 |
| 1954 | 10,985 | 7,466 | 3,519 | 8,743 | 1,519 | 32.0 | 79.6 | 13.8 |
| 1953 | 10,646 | 7,095 | 3,551 | 8,397 | 1,439 | 33.4 | 78.9 | 13.5 |
| 1952 | 10,273 | 6,839 | 3,433 | 8,013 | 1,411 | 33.4 | 78.0 | 13.7 |
| 1951 | 9,689 | 6,481 | 3,208 | 7,457 | 1,439 | 33.1 | 77.0 | 14.8 |
| 1950 | 8,480 | 5,603 | 2,876 | 6,282 | 1,397 | 33.9 | 74.1 | 16.5 |
| 1949 | 7,547 | 4,986 | 2,561 | 5,420 | 1,273 | 33.9 | 71.8 | 16.9 |
| 1948 | 7,179 | 4,589 | 2,590 | 5,148 | 1,221 | 36.1 | 71.7 | 17.0 |
| 1947 | 6,733 | 3,770 | 2,963 | 4,582 | 1,083 | 44.0 | 68.0 | 16.1 |
| 1946 | 6,190 | 3,808 | 2,383 | 4,153 | 1,038 | 38.5 | 67.1 | 16.8 |
| 1945 | 5,902 | 3,888 | 2,014 | 4,042 | 1,062 | 34.1 | 68.5 | 18.0 |
| 1944 | 5,614 | 3,650 | 1,964 | 3,815 | 883 | 35.0 | 68.0 | 15.7 |
| 1943 | 5,161 | 3,227 | 1,934 | 3,516 | 885 | 37.5 | 68.1 | 17.1 |
| 1942 | 4,454 | 2,885 | 1,569 | 3,146 | 753 | 35.2 | 70.6 | 16.9 |
| 1941 | 4,104 | 2,491 | 1,613 | 2,894 | 644 | 39.3 | 70.5 | 15.7 |
| 1940 | 3,694 | 2,095 | 1,599 | 2,734 | 863 | 43.3 | 74.0 | 9.8 |
| 1939 | 3,334 | 1,833 | 1,501 | 2,538 | 171 | 45.0 | 76.1 | 5.1 |
| 1938 | 3,061 | 1,567 | 1,494 | 2,358 | 101 | 48.8 | 77.0 | 3.3 |
| 1937 | 2,939 | 1,614 | 1,326 | 2,473 | 85 | 45.1 | 84.1 | 2.9 |
| 1936 | 2,645 | 1,484 | 1,161 | 2,225 | 74 | 43.9 | 84.1 | 2.8 |
| 1935 | 2,498 | 1,493 | 1,005 | 1,969 | 90 | 40.2 | 78.8 | 3.6 |

SOURCE: U. S. Department of the Interior, Bureau of Mines.

This does not weaken the plausibility of the 1.2 quadrillion cubic feet total future supply estimate. The key assumption on which this is based is a higher gas-oil ratio in the future than in the past. It was not possible to determine whether the higher ratio would be due to geologic factors at depth or to the influence of economic factors (e.g., the price of gas) on gas discovery; the adoption of 22.5 trillion cubic feet as the availability in 1975 stems from this open question. If depth is the basic determinant, then the limitation of oil output on gas output is called more strongly into play (i.e., the gas-oil ratio will be higher because *more gas with oil,* as well as more gas reservoirs, occurs at depth). But if price is fundamental, then the plausibility of an output level above 22.5 trillion is increased (i.e., the gas-oil ratio can be greater if exploration for gas *per se* is stimulated by a higher price, and more unassociated gas discoveries are made relative to total oil discoveries).

A word should be added concerning net availability. The discussion here has been in terms of what the Bureau of Mines calls "total gross withdrawal," or the quantity of gas produced at the wellhead, equivalent to gross availability. Column (d) of Table 16 shows the "marketed production" of natural gas, or the quantity actually sold, and column (e) shows the gas put back in the reservoir for pressure maintenance. (The quantity lost, wasted and consumed in production is not shown on the table.) Columns (g) and (h) list these two quantities as percentage of gross withdrawals. It will be seen that there was a marked decline in the proportion of gas withdrawals marketed (equivalent to net availability) during the first half of the preceding twenty years, with a subsequent return almost to the earlier level. In the earlier years of the period most of the non-marketed gas was wasted. The recent rise in the marketed proportion, despite the rise in repressuring (column h), reflects the adoption of gas conservation measures. It can be expected that in the period through 1975 the proportion of total withdrawals wasted will further decline, so that virtually all of the withdrawals not marketed will represent repressuring use, the course of which has been the opposite of marketed production relative to total gross withdrawals. The earlier rise is also due to conservation measures; the more recent decline can be ascribed to the postwar growth of nonassociated gas output The course of this relation in the future again depends on the place of associated and dissolved gas output in the total. It seems reasonable to conclude that net availability, because of repressuring, should range between 10 and 15 per cent lower than gross withdrawals in 1975.

## OTHER SOURCES OF SUPPLY

*Imports*

As was true of crude oil, allowance must also be made for imports as an element of total natural gas supply, for there is no reason to assume that domestic supply will satisfy demand in 1975, regardless of the level of demand. On the contrary, regional factors in the supply and demand of natural gas generate strong pressures towards the international movement of natural gas in North America.

In contrast to oil imports, natural gas imports have been negligible to date. As reported by the Bureau of Mines, imports as a percentage of total supply were 0.09 per cent in 1952, 0.10 per cent in 1953, 0.07 per cent in 1954, and 0.11 per cent in 1955. Large-scale contracts for imports from both Canada and Mexico over a twenty-year period have, however, already been entered into, and these indicate that in the coming decades foreign supply should become a formidable competitor to domestic supply in several important regions of the country.

The export potential of Canada has been assessed for that country's own purposes in a study sponsored by the Royal

Commission on Canada's Economic Prospects. According to this study, Canada could sustain an annual export level to the United States of one trillion cubic feet in the 1975 period without affecting supply or price in the domestic (Canadian) market. This is also considered the upper limit that could be contracted for without endangering the Canadian supply position after 1980.[28]

No equivalent figures are available concerning the import possibilities from Mexico in 1975. Although such imports might rise, there is no basis on which to make a quantitative estimate of their growth.

In addition to gas imports received via the traditional pipeline method of transportation, there is the revolutionary possibility involving the transport of natural gas by barge or tanker. This procedure, which has been demonstrated during the past few years to be economically feasible, involves liquefying the natural gas in the field at a temperature of approximately minus 260°F. and transporting it in the liquid state in insulated tanks, at atmospheric pressure, using the vapor from the liquid gas as fuel for the voyage. The gas is transferred to storage tanks at the market terminal still in the liquid state; it is delivered to consumers in the gaseous state, and in the process of vaporizing at the terminal it absorbs large quantities of heat. (Each 20,000-22,000 cubic feet of gas evaporated and warmed provides one ton of refrigeration capacity.) [29] With suitable arrangements this by-product refrigeration capacity can be utilized for such operations as cold-storage warehousing or the liquefaction of air (the latter could be marketed in turn or could be used on the spot in a petrochemical plant based on the natural gas).

The water-transport approach for liquefied gas has undergone pilot operations in this country and there appears to be considerable interest in the development of the method in

[28] J. Davis, *Canadian Energy Prospects* (Ottawa: Royal Commission on Canada's Economic Prospects, 1957), p. 182.
[29] *Power Engineering*, June, 1954, pp. 92 f.

several parts of the world.[30] One rather detailed analysis of the economics and technical problems concludes that "the proposed system under the worst conditions equals the present system of pipeline transmission."[31] According to this same study, the major physical problems concern the choice and design of container and insulating materials and the establishment of water transport safety standards.[32]

In the present context the significance of the concept of transporting liquefied gas by water is that it is applicable to the importation of natural gas from the oilfields of Venezuela. Although initial development of natural gas liquids recovery units (see below) and petrochemical plants is now beginning in Venezuela, such development will have to go a long way to absorb the available supply—70 per cent of the total yearly gas output of nearly one trillion cubic feet is currently flared.

The more remote possibility of gas imports from the Middle East should also be mentioned. Gas wastage in the Middle East is much greater: 500 million cubic feet per day in Saudi Arabia alone. It has been estimated that at current rates of crude production the Middle East as a whole could supply at least 1.5 billion cubic feet per day.[33] There is talk of getting the gas to energy-hungry Europe, and the possibility of liquefied natural gas imports from the Middle East to the United States by 1975 is not inconceivable.

In addition to his general analysis of the subject referred to above, Crecca, an authority on the water transport of

[30] For example, according to a recent report the Japanese were attempting to work out a project to import liquefied natural gas by tanker from Borneo, Sumatra, and other Southeast Asian sources, and even from Iran (*Petroleum Week*, July 5, 1957, p. 50, and September 27, 1957, p. 51).

Another report describes British plans for the importation of liquefied natural gas from Venezuela on a commercial scale beginning in 1959 (*Gas Age*, 120, No. 10 [November 14, 1957], 13, and *Petroleum Week*, December 20, 1957, p. 47).

[31] J. D. Crecca, Jr., "Liquid Gas . . . an Investigation" (Part vi—Summary), *Gas Journal*, 287, No. 4853 (July 18, 1956), 177.

[32] *Idem*.

[33] G. Trypanis, "The Influence of Engineering Progress on the Oil Industry—Marine Engineering," paper presented at the summer meeting of the Institute of Petroleum, Folkestone, England, May 29—June 1, 1957.

liquefied natural gas, has also published an economic analysis of a theoretical project to supply the Philadelphia area with its gas needs from Venezuela. According to this study, a fleet of seven converted T-2 tankers could supply 16 billion cubic feet a year at a cost of 2.39¢ per therm (100,000 Btu).[34] Not only is this in the competitive range with pipeline-delivered gas, but the costs are based on pure methane. Methane has a lower liquefaction temperature than natural gas, which is an admixture of other hydrocarbons, hence the liquefaction costs would be greater. In addition, the figures contain no credit for by-product refrigeration.

There is, of course, no means at present of foretelling whether importation of liquefied natural gas by water transport will ever come to pass, or if it does, when and on what scale. Evidence to date, however, indicates that this means of supply is technically and economically feasible on a significant scale. As such it is an important potential source.

In view of the above discussion it can be concluded that a considerable expansion in natural gas imports could take place, both absolutely and relative to total domestic consumption. The growth of imports from contiguous countries will be determined by supply-demand relationships and government export policies in those countries. Overseas imports involve technology, in addition. If they become a reality their growth would be influenced both by world market circumstances and by U. S. import policy.

## Price Aspects

At this point it is necessary to make some observations concerning price. The assumption has been made throughout the discussion of both crude oil and natural gas that con-

---

[34] J. D. Crecca, Jr., "Venezuelan Natural Gas for U. S.?" *Oil and Gas Journal*, LIV, No. 81 (November 19, 1956), 255, 257.

Economic feasibility is also indicated for the New York area by a more recent study (see P. B. Lederman and B. Williams, "Economics of Gas Liquefaction," *Gas Age*, 120, No. 10 [November 14, 1957], 41-47).

stant dollar costs will not increase significantly, but this does
not mean that the price of gas will also be stable. In the past
five years there has been a very rapid rise in the price of
natural gas. This is less related to costs, however, than to
market forces. Gas is a premium fuel in that it supplies
Btu's at the burner with high efficiency and with unequalled
convenience and cleanliness. With large over-capacity in the
field in earlier years due to lack of transmission facilities,
the price of natural gas could not reflect this premium value;
but with the development of markets based on its premium
characteristics, price has come to reflect such value.

The recent rise in the price of natural gas has been by
any standards both large and rapid. The average price at the
wellhead for the years 1946–50 was 6.2¢ per thousand cubic
feet. In 1954 it was 10.1¢, in 1956 it has been estimated at
not less than 12¢, with new contracts running as high as
22.5¢ and reserves being valued as high as 40¢.[35] The average
value at the point of consumption (obtained by dividing sales
volume into revenues received from consumers) was 24.5¢
per thousand cubic feet for the 1946–50 period. By 1954 this
had risen to 38.0¢ and the indicated value in 1955 was approximately 45¢.[36] (These national averages conceal wide
regional ranges which result from the regional nature of gas
markets and the variation that exists in field prices. A consideration of the regional aspects is, however, a study in itself, and it is believed that the figures above are meaningful
as first-order approximations.)

Such an upward trend in both field and delivered prices
cannot, of course, continue indefinitely, although some existing contracts contain escalation provisions reaching 36.4¢
in 1986. A continued rise in the average wellhead value will
further stimulate discovery and will tend to increase the import potential, but a rise in the average delivered value will

[35] A. K. Lee, "A Simple Solution for the Gas Producer Problem," *Public
Utilities Fortnightly*, LVIII, No. 7 (September 27, 1956), 442; also T. P. Walker,
"Some Comments on Gas Supply," *Public Utilities Fortnightly*, LVIII, No. 9
(October 25, 1956), 675.
[36] American Gas Association, *Gas Facts, 1955*, Chart 5, p. 28.

adversely affect the competitive position of natural gas versus other fuels despite the somewhat inelastic character of residential demand. This stems from the market pattern of natural gas. Large-volume industrial consumers account for somewhat more than half of the total natural gas consumption. They are able to use the gas at a much lower price than the residential and commercial retail price not only because the cost of distribution to them is lower but because their consumption is complementary to residential and commercial use. The latter uses fluctuate widely in their requirements, especially between seasons, so that their annual load factor is on the order of 40 per cent. But transmission pipelines must operate as close to 100 per cent load factor as possible, and industrial sales are the means by which this is accomplished. The development of underground storage to offset the seasonal peaking of residential and commercial consumption has been helpful in this respect, but it can replace only a portion of industrial consumption. The gas quantities involved—as much as 60 per cent of the total pipeline throughput—are simply too great for underground storage to be the entire solution to the peaking problem.

Yet industrial consumption of natural gas is highly elastic —it responds quickly and significantly to changes in the relative price of natural gas compared to that of competing fuels. Thus wherever and whenever the gas price approaches that of its competitors in following an upward trend it can be expected that industrial consumption will fall off.[37] To the extent that such industrial sales no longer help carry the fixed charges on transmission and distribution systems, those charges must be taken on by the residential and commercial customers. Hence, at a certain level in a rising price trend, the effect on the prices to the residential and commercial consumers will become magnified and the inelasticity of their

[37] See, for example, W. R. Connole, "Energy. Its Use and Abuse" (address given before the Independent Natural Gas Association of America, Houston, Texas, September 10, 1957), for a recent analysis of this prospect.

demand will tend to be offset. They, too, will begin to turn to competitive fuels.

In addition to these long-run market forces, there is the unresolved question of government regulation that remains at issue. The legislative outcome on this issue cannot be foreseen at this time, however, hence its possible effect on the price behavior of natural gas cannot be dealt with here.

## Synthetic Gas

Beyond this, in any event, there is the absolute ceiling set by synthetic gas. Oil and coal are, after all, not complete substitutes for gas, and to the extent that they are not there remains a market for certain specific gas uses at almost any price. But synthetic gas can be a total substitute for natural gas, and, given the proper price relationships, could completely replace it. The competitive relationship between synthetic and natural gas is rather complicated and necessitates some preliminary explanation.

Unlike synthetic liquid fuels, synthetic gas is not only a consideration for the future but has been important in the past. Indeed, synthetic gas preceded natural gas by a century as the major gaseous fuel in this country. The synthetic gas of the past and present, commonly termed "manufactured gas," is produced by several processes which depend in one way or another on coke or oil as the basis. These processes are, however, no longer economically feasible as means of supplying a full substitute for natural gas due to a number of circumstances. Natural gas is generally cheaper; at the same time the costs of coking coal and its shipment, and the operating costs of the gas-making process have all risen.

There is also an important physical distinction. The major constituent of natural gas is methane, a simple hydrocarbon compound. The major constituents of manufactured gas, on the other hand, are hydrogen and carbon monoxide (although under proper conditions these constituents can be synthesized into methane). The monetary value of any fuel gas is determined by its energy content, which is measured in British thermal units per cubic foot and is termed the "heat value" of the gas. Manufactured gas has an average heat value of 500-600 Btu per cubic foot, whereas natural gas averages 1,035 Btu per cubic foot, as marketed.

The emergence of natural gas in generally available supply throughout the United States has meant that any competitive gaseous fuel should preferably be in the same range of heat value. That is, in order to utilize pipeline transportation and to avoid changeover problems in gas-burning equipment, the alternative gas should have a heat value between 750 and 1,000 Btu per cubic foot,[38] a specific gravity in the same range as natural gas, and burning characteristics comparable to those of natural gas. A high-Btu gas is necessary for pipeline operations because the gas must have a high value to sustain the cost of pipeline transmission; or, to put it another way, the pipeline must have a high throughput of energy, not just gas volume. It is possible to produce such a gas from any hydrocarbon material in the form of a product which is, like natural gas, predominantly or almost wholly methane. Such a gas may be considered the synthetic equivalent of the natural product.

Synthetic gas from crude oil or its products, known as "oil gas," is currently used as a gas source in certain areas, but only for meeting peak needs or to enrich manufactured gas. Its production is carried on near the market, since it is cheaper to transport Btu's as oil, either by tanker or pipeline, than to transport Btu's as gas. The use of oil gas on a national scale to supply firm demand can be considered unlikely, however, since natural gas should be in relatively abundant supply through 1975. Indeed, such use of oil gas would involve a major revolution in the prices of all petroleum products, for a large increase in the demand for re-

[38] J. E. Tobey, "Gasification—Significance to the Bituminous Coal Industry," *Gasification and Liquefaction of Coal* (New York: American Institute of Mining and Metallurgical Engineers, 1953), pp. 207-209.

finery products suitable for gasification would seriously alter the refinery product mix. Oil gas is therefore ruled out of the discussion, leaving coal and oil shale as the sources to be considered.

The production of synthetic gas from coal on a large scale would not raise any problems of coal supply on the national level, but there are nevertheless locational limitations imposed by the requirements of individual plants. Roughly 100 pounds of coal are needed per thousand cubic feet of high-Btu gas produced. The present indicated economic minimum capacity for a coal gasification plant is about 100 million cubic feet daily, and the average would more likely be 200 million cubic feet. At the latter size, coal consumption would amount to 10,000 tons a day.[39] This necessitates that gasification be carried out close to the coal mine and that coal be used directly (i.e., without an intermediate stage such as coke). The gas, in turn, must therefore be supplied to most markets via long-distance pipeline, since market areas and coalfields do not generally coincide.[40]

Pilot-plant operation has indicated promise in two approaches to coal gasification in this country. One is a two-stage process that produces first a low-Btu gas which is catalytically methanated to a high-Btu pipeline gas. The other is a direct hydrogenation process in which "two of three elements of bituminous coal are converted directly to pipeline gas under proper pressure and temperature conditions, perhaps in the presence of a catalyst, with the third element used as a source of heat." [41] Both of these processes are suitable for base-load operation; indeed, they require a high load factor.

Other processes have been investigated or conceived in

[39] W. Gumz and J. F. Foster, *A Critical Survey of Methods of Making a High BTU Gas from Coal*, Research Bulletin No. 6, American Gas Association, July, 1953, p. 36.

[40] W. C. Schroeder, "Chemicals, Pipeline Gas, and Liquid Fuels from Coal," *Transactions*, Tenth Annual Anthracite Conference of Lehigh University, May 8 and 9, 1952, p. 42.

[41] W. B. Tippy, "Some Aspects of Gas Supply," paper presented at Executive Conference, American Gas Association, Colorado Springs, June 21, 1956.

attempts to reduce or eliminate the biggest economic obstacles to large-scale coal gasification—the cost of coal and the cost of the gasification process itself. Coal is a major item in the total cost of synthetic gas, and each one dollar increase in its cost per ton means an increase in the gas cost of six cents per thousand cubic feet.[42] The mining cost could be eliminated entirely through gasification of the coal underground, in place, but the general Btu content of the resultant gas would be very low, even if oxygen were employed. Considerable upgrading would thus be required to obtain a pipeline gas. Although continuing experiments are being carried out both in this country and abroad, the work is in such an early stage that commercial possibilities cannot yet be weighed.

A revolutionary attack on the gasification cost problem is to use a nuclear reactor as the source of heat. The basic limitation on the heat obtainable from a nuclear reactor is not the fuel input but the limits put on the operating temperature by the materials used in the reactor. The bulk heat output of a reactor thus suggests that this might be a fruitful means of reducing gasification costs. (In a two-stage process, the cost of the low-Btu initial gas is about 80 per cent of the total cost of the high-Btu product.) [43] At present, this approach is still in the conceptual design stage, hence is not considered here as a commercial possibility in the period through 1975.

The supply of high-Btu gas from oil shale can be obtained in two ways: as a by-product of synthetic liquid fuel manufacture, and in addition through the gasification of shale oil. To a significant degree, by-product supply suffers from the serious limitation of the scale of synthetic liquid fuel production. To be an important source of by-product gas, oil shale operations would have to be on such a scale as to con-

[42] C. F. De Mey, "Study of Synthetic Natural Gas," *American Gas Association Monthly*, xxxiv, No. 11 (November, 1952), 28.

[43] U. S. Department of Interior, Bureau of Mines, *Synthetic Liquid Fuels*, Part i, "Oil from Coal" (Report of Investigations 5043), April, 1954, p. iv.

tribute a substantial portion of the nation's liquid fuel supply. At the two-million barrel-a-day feasibility limit for shale oil operations discussed in the section on crude oil, the by-product gas from shale oil refining would amount to about 500 million cubic feet annually, only a small percentage of marketed production of natural gas in 1956. This by-product would be available, moreover, only from thermal cracking,[44] an obsolescent process for gasoline production.

It has been claimed that full gasification of shale oil, either at the mine or in the market area at the end of a shale oil pipeline, would be economically feasible,[45] but there remains the market problem of the by-products of the oil gasification. The value of by-product tar and light oils in the face of a vastly expanded supply could be so low as to make insignificant the credit from their sale that could be applied to the cost of the gas.

Table 17 summarizes the recent estimates of the cost of synthetic gas from coal and from oil shale. The estimates lack equivalence in several respects: (a) most pertain to the cost of synthetic gas at the fuel source, but some refer to the cost at the city gate (i.e., at the market but prior to distribution); (b) the estimates vary in the specified Btu content of the gas, but where possible, this has been offset through conversion to a common basis—cost per million Btu; (c) the assumed coal cost is variable—specified costs range from $2.00 to $6.07 per ton (reflecting locational differences, different ranks and grades, and price changes over time); (d) costs are expressed in current dollars; (e) some estimates are specific as to process, others are general.

General equivalence has been provided through conversion of the estimates to a common basis of cost per million Btu.

[44] U. S. Department of Interior, Bureau of Mines, *Synthetic Liquid Fuels*, Part II, "Oil from Oil Shale" (Report of Investigations 4866), July, 1952, pp. 44-47.
[45] H. M. Henry, "Where Will New England Get Its Future Gas Supply?" *Gas*, XXXI, No. 4 (April, 1955), 71-76.

TABLE 17

## Cost Estimates for Synthetic Gas

| Source | Date | Cost estimate | | Btu content |
|---|---|---|---|---|
| | | ¢/Mcf | ¢/MMBtu | |
| *GAS FROM COAL* | | | | |
| Foster & Vorum (a) | 1950 | 65.6 | 82 | 800 |
| | | 71.2-77.6 | 89-97 | 800 |
| | | 40 | 50 | 800 |
| Alberts *et al.* (b) (Blaw-Knox) | 10/52 | 55.35 | <61.5 | 900+ |
| De Mey (c) | 11/52 | 55-65 | <61.1-<72.2 | 900+ |
| Gumz & Foster (d) | 7/53 | 58.1 | 58.1-72.6 | 800-1,000 |
| | | 48.8 | 48.8-61.0 | 800-1,000 |
| | | 45.6 | 45.6-57.0 | 800-1,000 |
| | | 58.1 | 58.1-72.6 | 800-1,000 |
| Breck (e) (Pittsburgh-Consolidated) | 1953 | 54.77* | 59.21* | 925 |
| | | 58.0** | 62.70** | 925 |
| Minet *et al.* (f) | 7/54 | 56 | 62.22 | 900 |
| Tippy (g) | 1/55 | 65-75 | 65-75 } | 1,000 assumed |
| | | 59 | 59 } | |
| Henry (h) (Pittsburgh-Consolidated) | 3/55 | — | 45-55 | "high" |
| Chandler (i) | 8/55 | 55-75 | 55-75 | 1,000 |
| Tippy (j) | 6/56 | — | 90-100 70-75 | "high" |
| Bureau of Mines (k) (R.I.5272) | 11/56 | 37.6 | 268.6 | } 140 |
| | | 32.0 | 228.6 | |

| Source | Place (source or market) | Remarks |
|---|---|---|
| Foster & Vorum | source | Oxygen use, upgraded from 454-Btu Lurgi gas. |
| | market | Same, delivered 250-500 miles. |
| | source | Hypothetical single stage, high pressure process with 80 per cent thermal efficiency. |
| Alberts *et al.* (Blaw-Knox) | source | Lurgi plus catalytic methanation. Fuel cost $4/ton. Capital return 6 per cent. By-product credit. |
| De Mey | source | Interpretation of preceding. Each dollar increment fuel cost means 6¢ increment in gas cost. |
| Gumz & Foster | source | Lurgi plus catalytic methanation, 1 atmosphere pressure. |
| | source | Using oxygen, 20 atmospheres pressure. |
| | source | Using oxygen, 85 atmospheres pressure. |
| | source | Pulverized coal, 20 atmospheres pressure, catalytic methanation with credit for all surplus steam. Fuel $4/ton. |
| Breck (Pittsburgh-Consolidated) | source source | Lurgi plus catalytic methanation, 1,200 lbs. pressure, char as fuel. Coal $3.70/ton, by-product credit. */100% load factor, **/90% load factor. |
| Minet *et al.* | source | Process unspecified. Char as fuel. Coal $6.07/ton (25.8¢/MMBtu) by-product credits. |
| Tippy | source | Cost of "natural gas equivalent," known techniques. |
| | source | Cost of "natural gas equivalent," research advance over 5-year period. |
| Henry (Pittsburgh-Consolidated) | source | Ultimate possibilities with unconventional gasification process. |
| Chandler | source | Bureau of Mines estimate using heat from nuclear reactor for gasification. 250-300 Btu gas, subsequently upgraded. Upgrading costs possibly lower than allowed for. |
| Tippy | source | Current indications for two-stage process "possibility of improvement." |
| Bureau of Mines (R.I.5272) | source | Natural lignite @ $2/ton. 50 MM cu.ft./day plant, output $H_2$ and CO at ratio of 2.5:1. Same with steam-dried lignite @ $3.60/ton, $H_2$-CO ratio 2.0:1. |

TABLE 17

## Cost Estimates for Synthetic Gas (continued)

| Source | Date | Cost estimate | | Btu content |
|---|---|---|---|---|
| | | ¢/Mcf | ¢/MMBtu | |
| *UNDERGROUND GASIFICATION* | | | | |
| Gerdetz (l) | 11/53 | 3.297 | 11.648 | 283 |
| *GAS FROM OIL SHALE* | | | | |
| Bureau of Mines (m) | 7/52 | 14.8 | 13.96 | 1,060 |
| (R.I.4866) | | 18.2 | 14.00 | 1,300 |
| Henry (n) | 4/55 | 18.2 | 14.0 | 1,300 |
| | | 43.2 | 33.2 | 1,300 |
| | | 60-65 | 60-65 | 1,000 |

SOURCES:

(a) J. F. Foster and D. A. Vorum, "Pipe-Line (high Btu) Gas," *Economics of Fuel Gas from Coal*, ed. R. J. Lund and J. F. Foster (New York: McGraw-Hill Book Co., 1950), p. 103.

(b) L. W. Alberts *et al.*, "Production of Methane from Coal," *Chemical Engineering Progress*, XLVIII, No. 10 (October, 1952), 486-93.

(c) C. F. De Mey, "Study Synthetic Natural Gas," *American Gas Association Monthly*, XXXIV, No. 11 (November, 1952), 28.

(d) W. Gumz and J. F. Foster, *A Critical Survey of Methods of Making a High BTU Gas from Coal*, Research Bulletin No. 6 (New York: American Gas Association, July, 1953).

(e) C. R. Breck, "The Timing of an Initial Pipeline-gas-from-coal Enterprise," *Gasification and Liquefaction of Coal* (New York: American Institute of Mining and Metallurgical Engineers, 1953), pp. 189-94.

(f) R. G. Minet *et al.*, "Economics of Coal Carbonization by the Low-Temperature Process," *Chemical Engineering Progress*, L, No. 7 (July, 1954), 342-47.

| Source | Place (source or market) | Remarks |
|---|---|---|
| Gerdetz | source | Combined mining and underground gas operation. 20-25 per cent of coal mined and shipped. $4.50/ton coal to car and gas to collar. |
| Bureau of Mines (R.I.4866) | market market | By-products of thermal cracking of shale oil at California end of pipeline. |
| Henry | market | At refinery, St. Louis, gas as by-product. |
|  | market | At refinery, New England, allowing 20-25¢/ Mcf transportation costs, using new pipelines. |
|  | market | Gas manufactured in New England from landed shale oil at $2.50/bbl. Gasification bearing all charges, less by-product credits. |

(g) W. B. Tippy, "What Will Happen to the Price of Gas?" *Gas,* xxxi, No. 1 (January, 1955), 40.

(h) H. M. Henry, "What About Gas Supply and Price?" *Gas Age,* 115, No. 5 (March 10, 1955), 25-49.

(i) M. Chandler, "Outlook for Gas Industry," *Gas Age,* 116, No. 4 (August 25, 1955), 24 f.

(j) W. B. Tippy, "Some Aspects of Gas Supply," paper presented at Executive Conference, American Gas Association, Colorado Springs, June 21, 1956.

(k) O. C. Ongstad, M. H. Chetrick, and W. H. Oppelt, *Cost Data for Gasification of Lignite in an Externally Heated Retort* (U. S. Department of Interior, Bureau of Mines, Report of Investigations 5272), pp. 8-10.

(l) L. F. Gerdetz, "Controlled Underground Gasification," *Coal Age,* lviii, No. 11 (November, 1953), 80 ff.

(m) U. S. Department of Interior, Bureau of Mines, *Synthetic Liquid Fuels, Annual Report of the Secretary of the Interior for 1951,* Part ii, *Oil From Oil Shale* (Report of Investigations 4866, July, 1952, p. 53.

(n) H. M. Henry, "Where Will New England Get Its Future Gas Supplies?" *Gas,* xxxi, No. 4 (April, 1955), 71-76.

Nevertheless, due to the wide variation in the technical details from which the estimates are derived, it is impossible to compare them individually without becoming involved in an extensive technical discussion. But this is not necessary, since all that is needed is a rough approximation of the cost level of synthetic gas as a competitor with natural gas.

Estimates for underground gasification and gasification involving nuclear reactors can be eliminated at this point. Because of their very early stage of development, these processes can be considered only as possibilities rather than probabilities for the period with which this study is concerned. Shale oil can likewise be ruled out as a significant source, because of the limitations of the by-product aspect, although it could, like crude oil, have local importance.

It is evident from the remaining estimates of Table 17 that there is a wide range of disagreement among the experts, even allowing for changes in the price level between 1950 and 1956. At the one extreme are estimates up to $1 per million Btu, representing, in general, costs as they are now seen. At the other extreme are estimates ranging down to less than 50¢, expressing the expectations of their authors as to the results of future technological progress.

As a useful middle ground, a figure of 65¢ per million Btu can be used to express the general level of the cost at which it might be possible to produce synthetic gas in volume, in the coal field, in the period through 1975.

An analysis of pipeline costs and rate structures indicates that the average cost for gas transport is about 1.5¢ per Mcf per 100 miles.[46] Assuming the distance from coal fields to major gas consuming centers would range between 100 and 500 miles, the cost of synthetic gas transport would be from 1.5¢ to 7.5¢ per Mcf. It was concluded above that the average cost of synthetic gas at the point of production, with present technology, is likely to be 65¢ per million Btu. Assuming for

---

[46] F. K. Edwards, "The Relative Position of Coal and Natural Gas as Competitive Fuels," paper presented at 1956 Spring Conference, Southeastern Association of Railroad and Utilities Commissioners, Miami Beach, April 6, 1956.

convenience that the product is 1,000-Btu pipeline gas, the cost of such synthetic gas at the city gate would be in the range of 66.5¢ to 72.5¢ per Mcf, or 70¢ as a round number.

In contrast, recent typical city-gate prices in the several market regions were as follows: [47]

| Consuming region | City-gate price (cents per Mcf) |
|---|---|
| New England ................ | 52 |
| Middle Atlantic .............. | 34 |
| South Atlantic .............. | 28 |
| North Central .............. | 27 |
| Pacific ..................... | 26 |
| Mountain ................... | 20 |

These figures suggest that on the average the city-gate price of natural gas would have to increase 2.5 times before synthetic gas would be competitive, while under the most favorable conditions (long natural gas transport distance versus short synthetic gas transport distance) the competitive level might be less than 50 per cent above the present city-gate price in certain areas. At the same time, as the price of natural gas continued to rise, efforts to reduce the cost of synthetic gas would be intensified, and if the more optimistic estimates in Table 17 are correct, there would begin to be competitive synthetic gas production on a large scale at something like a two-thirds increase in the average city-gate price of natural gas. Well before that, because of the wide regional range of city-gate prices, there would be local opportunities for synthetic gas, as well as further expansion in the current use of oil gas for peak shaving.

It can be concluded, therefore, that if the price of natural gas undergoes further rise during the period through 1975,

[47] H. D. Ralph, "Price Is the Key to Growth of Gas," *Oil and Gas Journal,* LIV, No. 12 (July 25, 1955), 165.

the rate of increase should taper off markedly as local market competition from other fuels becomes more effective. And without a significant decline in the cost of synthetic gas (which cannot be foreseen at this time) synthetic is unlikely to provide more than minor local competition by 1975. Nevertheless the price of synthetic gas, at whatever level it may be during the period, will constitute a potential ceiling on the price of natural gas.

# I I I

# natural gas liquids

## DEFINITION, OCCURRENCE, AND USE

Natural gas was described in the previous section as consisting principally of methane, which is the simplest in the series of hydrocarbon compounds known as the "paraffin series." The remaining constituents of natural gas, other than non-hydrocarbon impurities, are additional, heavier members of the paraffin series. These compounds have the property of either liquefying spontaneously at atmospheric temperature and pressure or else being amenable to liquefaction through simple pressure-temperature manipulation. Because this property is utilized to obtain them in liquid form these compounds are known as "natural gas liquids" (abbreviated NGL). Their relative proportion, both singly and in sum, as constituents of natural gas is highly variable among reservoirs, and is in some measure determined by production methods. Their total proportion may be virtually zero, in which instance the natural gas is known as a "dry" gas. A "wet" gas has the following typical proportions (in per cent by volume): methane, 80-90 per cent; ethane, 5-10 per cent; propane, 3-5 per cent; isobutane and butane, 1-2 per cent; pentane and the heavier members of the paraffin series, 1-2 per cent.[1]

[1] B. R. Carney, "Natural Gas Liquids," *Progress in Petroleum Technology* (Washington, D. C.: American Chemical Society, 1951), p. 255.

Natural gas liquids, or NGL, as the source of many of the same hydrocarbon compounds obtainable from crude oil, are often lumped with the latter, especially in discussions of reserves and total production, under the term "liquid hydrocarbons," and the word "petroleum" has also been used synonymously with liquid hydrocarbons. Although from this point of view NGL might have been better discussed in the chapter on crude oil, the fact remains that they are a constituent of natural gas, hence their long-term supply is a function of natural gas supply. Moreover, as a hydrocarbon resource they are not synonymous with crude oil. They are, as will be seen, a source of a variety of hydrocarbon raw materials and products, but many of their uses are specific. In the broad sense they may be considered competitive with crude oil (some NGL are refinery feedstock), but they are really more supplementary to crude oil as a resource than as an alternative, as is shale oil.[2]

It should also be understood that NGL are anomalous in that they do not constitute a net addition to energy resources. They are by common practice included in natural gas reserve data in both physical (quantity) and energy terms. A gas reserve or resource estimate includes among the X trillion cubic feet of the figure the cubic feet of NGL which are present in the reservoir in the gaseous phase; and the standard figure of 1,075 Btu/cubic feet used as the heat value of natural gas at the wellhead includes the energy content of the NGL. But since NGL do constitute an alternative source of some petroleum products it is appropriate to consider them here in terms of their separate future supply.

NGL are commonly divided into three categories in a classification scheme which is confusing not only because the categories overlap but because the classification is based on both mode of occurrence and type of use. The classification

---

[2] Since NGL correspond to the saleable (as opposed to residual) products from crude oil, they are equivalent to a larger unit liquid volume of crude. It has been estimated that one barrel of NGL displaces 1¼ barrels of crude in consumption. (*Petroleum Week,* November 22, 1957, p. 11.)

is nevertheless important in any analysis of future supply probabilities.

One category consists of propane, isobutane, and butane, compounds which are gases at atmospheric pressure and temperature but are readily liquefied. Although they are extracted and handled in the liquid state they are consumed as fuel in the gaseous state, hence their designation "liquefied petroleum gases" (commonly abbreviated as LPG). A second category includes isobutane, butane, pentane and heavier members which constitute a liquid mixture at ordinary temperatures and pressures. This mixture closely corresponds to manufactured gasoline and although it has a low octane number can be readily used as such, hence the term "natural gasoline." The third category consists of heavier paraffin series compounds which are also gaseous under high pressure and temperature in the reservoir, but which condense to a liquid under lower temperature-pressure conditions. These are known as "condensate."

Although the occurrence of NGL is highly variable, certain characteristics are significant in the present context. Associated gas is "wet" gas. LPG and natural gasoline occur in all "wet" gas; condensate, on the other hand, occurs only in gas reservoirs with pressures above 2,000 pounds per square inch and temperatures above 200°F. Very few such reservoirs are found at depths of less than 6,000 feet.

Carney distinguishes four types of NGL production: [3] (1) *Gas field plants* extract NGL "to permit the satisfactory transportation and use of gas," and produce natural gasoline and condensate, with some LPG (propane and butane). (2) *Oil field plants* yield a similar product mix (except for condensate) in processing casinghead gas incident to oil production. (3) *Cycling plants* strip condensate and usually some LPG (propane and butane) from gas that is then returned to the reservoir. (4) *Gas wells* produce condensate, known as "lease condensate," at the wellhead due to the reduction

[3] Carney, *loc. cit.*

in pressure and temperature at the wellhead in the course of gas production.

The uses of the three categories of NGL are also to some extent overlapping. The chief use of LPG is as a domestic and commercial fuel for heating and cooking. Other uses are chemical manufacturing, internal combustion engine fuel (directly, as well as a raw material), synthetic rubber manufacture, and general industrial uses, in that order. A peculiar feature of the LPG market is that there is direct competition from similar compounds produced by petroleum refineries (sometimes called liquefied refinery gases, or LRG). Currently about 30 per cent of the total supply of marketable LPG is from this source. Natural gasoline is used as a blend stock in motor fuel manufacture. The condensate liquids serve as petro-chemical feedstock.

## RESERVES AND FUTURE SUPPLY ESTIMATES

The anomalous nature of NGL as an energy source is further evident in the definition of proved reserves used by the American Gas Association. "Proved recoverable reserves of natural gas liquids are those contained in the recoverable gas reserves subject to being produced as natural gas liquids by separators or extraction plants, now in operation, under construction or planned for the immediate future." [4] In other words, not only is the current recoverability limitation included in the reserve definition, as in natural gas and crude oil, but in addition the limitation of current productive capacity is further used.

This new limitation, which at first glance seems unnecessarily restrictive, nevertheless has its rationale. As noted at the beginning of this study, the reserve concept is universally limited to what is currently economic. In one sense, natural

[4] 1957 Report of the Committee on Natural Gas Reserves of the American Gas Association.

gas liquids in reservoirs for which no extractive capacity exists are *not* economically recoverable at present. This cannot be taken too literally, but it would appear to be a pertinent generalization. Moreover, there is not the simple situation that there is with respect to most mineral raw materials —that anything not recoverable today is potentially recoverable in the future (either *in situ* or in a waste dump) at some cost. The fact is, NGL not currently recovered do not remain in the reservoir (except for what are not recovered in cycling) but are permanently removed from the reservoir along with the oil or gas that contains them. Indeed, one cannot say with certainty that even the total 5.9 billion barrels of currently proved NGL reserves will be produced as such. Depending on circumstances at the time of production (which will vary with each reservoir) they may be recorded as part of NGL, crude oil, or gas output.

Nevertheless, the concept of future NGL supply is not thereby meaningless, although estimates are understandably few. The only published estimate of total future NGL supply is for an "indicated" 10 billion barrels, on the assumption that "the future supply of natural-gas liquids will maintain the same relationship to natural-gas discoveries in the future as it does now." [5] The validity of this estimate is considered below.

The few published estimates of future NGL production are listed in Table 18. All were originally expressed in terms of the daily production rate, here rounded to the nearest 100,000 barrels and converted into an annual total rounded to the nearest 25 million barrels. The Batchelder and Nelson estimate was read from Chart 4 of their paper and is consistent with their statement that production should almost double by 1975. None of the authors offers any basis for his estimate. Pogue and Hill indicate that their figure for the "computed recovery" of NGL is in some way related to their

[5] J. R. Stockton, R. C. Henshaw, and R. W. Graves, *Economics of Natural Gas in Texas* (Austin: Bureau of Business Research, University of Texas, 1952), p. 149.

estimate of natural gas output, but the relation is not given. The Hill *et al.* estimate follows the statement that "should the market and price warrant, a substantially higher percentage of the liquid content of natural gas could be removed and utilized." With the exception of the earliest and most recent of the estimates, there is evident variation in opinion as to the likely level of future production.

TABLE 18

*Estimates of Future U.S. Production of*
*Natural Gas Liquids*

| Source and date | Year | Daily production (*mill. bbls.*) | Equivalent annual production (rounded) (*mill. bbls.*) | Index equivalent of 1955 production (1955=100) |
|---|---|---|---|---|
| Swearingen, 1952 (a) | 1967 | 1.5 | 550 | 158 |
| Cadle, 1955 (b) | 1975 | 1.4 | 500 | 148 |
| Batchelder & Nelson, 1955(c) | 1975 | 1.1 | 400 | 116 |
| Pogue & Hill, 1956 (d) | 1965 | 1.2 | 425 | 127 |
| Hill *et al.*, 1957 (e) | 1966 | 1.5 | 550 | 158 |

SOURCES:

(a) J. E. Swearingen, "Meeting Future Petroleum Demands," *Oil and Gas Journal,* November 17, 1952, pp. 328-36.

(b) A. Cadle, "An Appraisal of Future Energy Demand and Supply in the United States," paper given before American Petroleum Institute Petroleum Industry Buyers, San Francisco, November 15, 1955.

(c) H. R. Batchelder and H. W. Nelson, "Future of Synthetic Liquid and Gaseous Fuels," paper given before Joint Fuels Conference, Columbus, Ohio, October 19-20, 1955.

(d) J. E. Pogue and K. E. Hill, *Future Growth and Financial Requirements of the World Petroleum Industry* (New York: Chase Manhattan Bank, 1956). Presented at annual meeting of American Institute of Mining, Metallurgical and Petroleum Engineers, Petroleum Branch, February 21, 1956.

(e) K. E. Hill, H. D. Hammar, and J. G. Winger, *Future Growth of the World Petroleum Industry* (New York: Chase Manhattan Bank, 1957). Presented at meeting of American Petroleum Institute Division of Production, Rocky Mountain District, Casper, Wyoming, April 25, 1957.

# TECHNOLOGY AS A DETERMINANT OF

# FUTURE NGL AVAILABILITY

Statistics on recent NGL recovery are listed in Table 19. The first column shows the ratio of net production [6] of NGL, as reported by the American Gas Association, to the quantity of natural gas treated for NGL recovery, as reported by the Bureau of Mines. The second column shows the ratio of NGL recovery, as reported by the Bureau of Mines, to that agency's figure for natural gas treated.

TABLE 19

*NGL Recovery*

(In barrels per million cubic feet)

| Year | On A.G.A. Basis | Bureau of Mines figure |
|------|-----------------|------------------------|
| 1955 | 39.14 | 34.37 |
| 1954 | 40.33 | 33.12 |
| 1953 | 45.27 | 35.00 |
| 1952 | 44.36 | 34.76 |
| 1951 | 43.05 | 33.10 |
| 1950 | 42.53 | 34.05 |
| 1949 | 42.76 | 33.81 |
| 1948 | 41.82 | 33.83 |
| 1947 | 39.50 | 32.38 |
| 1946 | 35.28 | 31.67 |
| 1945 | n.a. | 32.62 |

Average 1950-55 ......42.45    Average 1950-55 ......34.07
Average 1946-50 ......40.40    Average 1945-49 ......32.86

[6] "Net production" is undefined beyond "permanent removal from the ground." It presumably excludes the unrecovered NGL content of cycled gas.

Neither of these ratios is a true representation. The American Gas Association net production figures cover production from all sources, but the Bureau of Mines excludes NGL burned in the field or which never reach a processing plant because of loss or waste, and does not count the liquids recovered at pipeline compressor stations and gas-dehydration plants. Thus the first ratio involves NGL recovery from a total gas output greater than that reported by the Bureau of Mines as treated, and overstates the true recovery level to an unknown degree. The Mines ratio, on the other hand, represents the true recovery within the coverage of the data, but the figures are biased downward on two counts. First, the data include such operations as the processing of gas at the pipeline transmission stage that has already been processed. The yield the second time around is, of course, bound to be very low, and would for this reason alone pull down any average in which it was included. But more than this, for a true measure of total recovery, the recovery through the second processing should be added to that obtained in the first processing, while the quantity of gas processed should be counted only once, not twice as is done in the Bureau of Mines statistics. Second, the Bureau of Mines data include the results of operations in which the recovery level is deliberately set lower than capability in order to match NGL output to low seasonal demand. To this extent the ratio is less a measure of current technological capability than of operating practice. Both ratio series listed in Table 19 are useful, nevertheless, as the upper and lower limits to the actual recovery level in a given year, whatever that may be. It cannot be more than the ratio based on net production; it cannot be less than the Bureau of Mines figure.

Whatever the recovery factor actually is, there is evidence that it is held down less by technological capability than by economic factors that determine the provision of extraction facilities and the extent to which existing facilities are fully utilized. Carney estimated in 1951 that a recovery factor equivalent to 51 barrels per million cubic feet was "well within the limits of present methods." "Other students of this problem," he continued, "have reported that a very much greater potential is available whenever the demand may justify. It is recognized that this increased recovery will be attended by higher costs than present recoveries." [7] From this it can be inferred that a recovery factor of 51 barrels is feasible at present costs, with still higher recoveries technically obtainable at higher costs. It is probable that the current technological limit at present costs is already higher than Carney's estimate as a result of process improvements and innovations in subsequent years.

## CONCLUSIONS ON DOMESTIC

## NGL AVAILABILITY

Just as the crucial element in considering the future supply of natural gas itself is the ratio of its occurrence to that of crude oil, so the ratio of natural gas liquids to natural gas is crucial in reaching conclusions on the future supply of NGL. In an analysis of 1950 NGL production, Carney used something over 60 barrels per million cubic feet as the ratio of occurrence in nature, "based on a study of a large number of representative gas analyses from principal producing areas in the Mid-Continent and Gulf Coast." [8] This estimate is taken as authoritative and is here rounded to 60 barrels per million cubic feet.

With this occurrence ratio it is possible to derive a resource-base estimate for NGL. Applied to the total future gas supply estimate of 1.2 quadrillion cubic feet it yields an NGL minimum resource base of 72 billion barrels. Aside

[7] Carney, *op. cit.*, p. 259 (*cf. op. cit.*, Table V, p. 256).
[8] *Idem.*

from the fact that the occurrence ratio was not applied to a natural gas resource-base estimate, the figure of 72 billion is conservative in that it is based on past experience. Condensate reservoirs are more frequent at depth, and if it is assumed that such reservoirs will constitute a higher proportion of future discoveries than in the past, the occurrence ratio could be greater than 60 barrels per million cubic feet. Ratios of 150 barrels have been reported for recent discoveries.

A reserve estimate can also be derived using Carney's data. Using the figure of 51 barrels per million cubic feet as the limit of current technology at current costs, NGL reserves ("discovered" and undiscovered) are on the order of 60 billion barrels as a probable minimum. In this light, the estimate of 10 billion barrels total future supply by Stockton, *et al.* is far too low, tied as it is to the NGL-gas ratio in discoveries. The ratio of 20 barrels per million cubic feet implied in this estimate was apparently assumed from the most recent data for new field and new pool discoveries at the time the estimate was made. (The ratio in such discoveries in 1950 was 20.2.)

Since NGL do not constitute a net addition to energy resources because of their inclusion in quantity figures for natural gas, it is worth noting the significance of the above NGL resource-base estimate in terms of a net estimate of future natural gas supply. In adjusting natural gas reserve figures for the currently feasible increase in NGL recovery, Carney uses an equivalence of 1,343 cubic feet per barrel.[9] That is, the production of one barrel of NGL removes 1,343 cubic feet from the gas stream carrying it. Although this adjustment was for increased recovery, hence represented different proportions of compounds than is true for NGL in general, it is sufficient to indicate the order of magnitude of the effect on natural gas volume. Applying it, accordingly, to the 72 billion barrel resource-base estimate, the result is 80.58 trillion cubic feet. It can be concluded from this that

[9] *Ibid.*, p. 260.

full exploitation of future NGL resources would reduce total future natural gas availability by less than 10 per cent.

The estimate of 1975 availability of NGL must also be derived from the estimate of 22.5 trillion cubic feet made above for natural gas availability in that year. Since there is no basis for determining the degree of technological progress in NGL recovery that could be expected in the period through 1975, the figure of 51 barrels per million cubic feet taken from Carney as the limit of current technology under current costs is assumed for 1975. This yields a figure of 1,148 million barrels as the domestic availability of NGL in that year. In view of the compounding of assumptions, this can be rounded to one billion barrels as an order of magnitude.

For purposes of comparison it may be noted that this is equivalent to almost three times the 1956 output level of NGL. But to reiterate—*the estimate is not for production.* The significance of the large magnitude is comparable to that of the oil availability estimate; it emphasizes the large recovery potential. The evidence at hand indicates that domestic sources could supply a market for natural gas liquids on the order of one billion barrels. Whether such a market is likely to exist is a matter for separate investigation.

## OTHER SOURCES OF SUPPLY

Natural gas liquids, especially LPG and natural gasoline, are well suited to pipeline and tank transport, the latter both land (rail and truck) as well as marine. Given sufficient economic impetus, there is always the possibility that the potential NGL supplies of Canada and Venezuela could be developed for the U. S. market. The recent government-sponsored study of the energy prospects of Canada foresees an NGL export availability from that country of 7 million barrels in 1965 and 20 million barrels in 1980.[10] No estimates of Venezuelan capability exist.

As noted above, there is only one direct substitute for any of the NGL components—liquefied refinery gases for liquefied petroleum gases. Hence only LPG can be considered to have an alternative "synthetic" source. Nevertheless, because NGL compete with crude oil as a source for both gasoline for the refinery gasoline pool and for petro-chemical feed stock, NGL prices must be competitive with the prices of crude oil and refinery products.

This could exercise a ceiling effect on NGL prices, but aside from this, it does not seem likely that NGL costs would exert any upward pressure on NGL prices. The discovery and production costs of natural gas from any of its types of occurrence do not enter into NGL costs, since NGL are wholly by-products. Indeed, with the spread of conservation laws that require the repressuring of casinghead gas there has been a tendency to install NGL recovery facilities so that the return on the NGL output can help defray, even if it does not fully cover, the cost of handling the gas.

The major production cost element is actual recovery, and here the record to date has been one of cost reduction, as recovery processes have been improved and made more efficient. Prime cost deterrents in NGL marketing to date have been transportation and storage, but here too costs have declined as facilities have been improved and economies of scale have been realized. The great handicap of highly seasonal demand for LPG can now be overcome with the development of large-scale storage, and the transportation handicap could be largely overcome by the installation of recovery plants at the terminals of long-distance transmission pipelines rather than in the field.

[10] J. Davis, *Canadian Energy Prospects* (Ottawa: Royal Commission on Canada's Economic Prospects, 1957), p. 192.

# index